INVEST IN LIVING

HOME RABBIT KEEPING

INVEST IN LIVING

HOME RABBIT KEEPING

by

MARJORIE E.P. NETHERWAY

EP Publishing Limited

Acknowledgements

I am indebted to the following for the illustrations:

Mr Hopcraft of Hopcraft, Photographers Ltd, Worcester, who took photographs of the outside hutches, by courtesy of Mrs Harding, Delamere Bird Garden, near Pershore, Worcs. Mr Hopcraft also took photographs of interior pens by courtesy of the Midland Counties Rabbit Company, Evesham, Worcs.

Other illustrations of pens, equipment and rabbits are by courtesy of Messrs Sydenham Hannaford Ltd, Poole, Dorset and Messrs BOCM Silcock Ltd, Stoke Mandeville, Bucks.

About the author

Marjorie Netherway SRN, first started keeping rabbits in 1945 when rationing was in force. Besides keeping meat varieties she was also successful in breeding show rabbits and became increasingly interested in the theoretical aspects of rabbit growth and characteristics.

From 1954 Mrs Netherway wrote for *Fur and Feather* and other weeklies, and also the rabbit advisory section of the old *Smallholder*. Following committee work on Rabbit Clubs and service as show secretary and manager, she restarted the rabbit section of the Three Counties Agricultural Show and ran it for several years.

In 1960 she was a founder member of the Worcestershire Commercial Rabbit Association. An early member of the national Commercial Rabbit Association, she served on its council and later as secretary; on retirement she was made the only Honorary Member of the association.

Mrs Netherway has remained active in the industry, writing articles and the *Manual of Rabbit Farming*, and doing advisory work through correspondence.

Contents

How to Start

Advantages of Home Rabbit Keeping

Rabbit keeping is fun as well as useful. A small animal, pleasant to handle, the rabbit can be kept with ease by older and handicapped persons as well as by the able bodied; ladies are especially noted for their success as rabbit keepers. The meat is easily digested, has a delicate flavour, and as there is very little fat it is particularly suitable for slimmers, children and old people. There are dozens of ways of cooking rabbit, winter and summer dishes as well as snacks and sandwiches; as there is no close season a supply of meat can be obtained all the year round.

The cost of keeping and rearing one's own rabbit meat can be adjusted to the amount of cash available. Some capital is necessary but a little skill and planning in setting up an efficient unit can keep this amount as low as possible. The owner of a smaller unit has more opportunity to make his own hutches or pens, and usually has time to undertake his own repairs and maintenance. It must be emphasised that keeping rabbits will not be successful if it is done 'on the cheap', which is vastly different from economising on outlay. Plan carefully, read about the subject and get in touch with other rabbit keepers in your area.

Town or Country Gardens

Neat hutches or pens can be sited in a quiet part of the garden or backyard. In town or small gardens wooden hutches with some protection from the weather are quite suitable, but in larger or country gardens the provision of a hut, shed or open barn should be considered, giving the rabbit keeper shelter as well as his rabbits. Some local authorities do not allow any livestock on council house estates, others permit a limited number under controlled rules, and this should be checked before you select the type of hutch or house. Usually there is no objection to a few tidy hutches in a sheltered spot, even in towns. Country authorities are more used to livestock and will probably be less rigid in their rules.

Indoor or Outdoor Units

This remains a matter of choice, taking into consideration local regulations, choice of site, materials available and capital outlay. The ideal type of rabbit unit consists of wire-mesh pens placed in a well-ventilated house. Outdoor hutches must be weatherproofed and have removable shutters to fit three-parts of the way up the wire fronts. Cats and dogs should be kept away from the hutches.

Indoor hutches or pens do not need shutters as long as the windows are covered with wire mesh to give protection against vermin, dogs etc., and you must be sure to have a good fastener on the house door. Indoor rabbits will probably give a better production figure as they will be less affected by weather changes; however, outdoor bred and reared rabbits are less likely to get colds or chest troubles. The final decision may depend on the availability of a house, for new houses are very expensive; but whether indoors or out, a comfortable, well-fed rabbit will thrive.

The rabbit house may be a disused poultry house, barn, shed, garage or a veranda-type shelter. It must be kept clean, free from rats or mice, dogs and cats, and flies must be kept to a minimum. Never, never let a wild rabbit get into the rabbit house; it could carry fleas and disease. The home rabbit keeper is unlikely to have a large number of rabbits housed in an ex-poultry house. The smaller the shed the more carefully the ventilation and number of pens must be calculated. It is not easy to keep plenty of fresh air flowing without direct draughts on the rabbits, but it must be managed somehow.

A block of outdoor hutches with solid wooden floors and wooden doors to the nesting areas. Each wire door has a board at the base to prevent bedding from falling out. There is no piped water supply, so bottle drinkers are used with tubes through the wire doors for the rabbits to suck. This unit uses pellet bowls because the more usual hoppers are not practical. The lattice work over the roof prevents cats from peering down on the top hutches

Ventilation

This is one of the most common causes of trouble in a rabbitry, for a steady flow of fresh air is essential for the rabbits' health. This flow should preferably be supplemented by an outlet in the roof. Most types of window can be baffled and, provided there is a wire-mesh covering, can be left open day and night, except in the event of snow, gales or other extreme conditions. Any outlet or inlet for air must be covered in wire mesh to keep out unwanted visitors, a mesh size of 19 × 19 mm ($\frac{3}{4}$ × $\frac{3}{4}$ in.) being suitable. A simple test for the atmosphere of the rabbit house is to take a good sniff when the door is first opened in the morning. It should smell sweet with a warm animal smell and have no obvious trace of ammonia fumes.

Space per Doe

The space allotted to each buck or growing rabbit includes, with the air space needed for health, the actual floor area of its pen. A pen with a wire-mesh floor which allows droppings to fall clear should be 900 × 600 × 450 mm (3 ft. × 2 ft. × 18 in.) high with an alley in front 0.9–1 m (3–$3\frac{1}{4}$ ft.) wide. This is the ideal, but in solid-floor hutches the rabbit's floor area must be increased to 1200 × 600 × 450 mm (4 ft. × 2 ft. × 18 in.) high to allow area for droppings. It is better to have outdoor hutches rather than cram too many rabbits into an inadequate shed.

The height of the shed roof from the floor can make a lot of difference to the comfort of the stock. If it is too high, the shed may be cold in winter and if too low, too hot in summer. Ceilings should be 2.5–3 m (8– 10 ft.) above ground level, a convenient height, too, for the placing of light sockets.

Pens and Hutches

Strictly speaking the terms are interchangeable, but those with solid walls and roof, usually wood, are called hutches and those with an all wire-mesh construction are pens. The modern hutch can be fitted with a wire-mesh floor with a tray beneath to catch the droppings. Hutches must be weatherproof for outside use, pens must always be kept indoors.

Construction and Materials

The hutch for outdoor use is made of wooden walls and roof, other materials being less satisfactory as they need heavy insulation to keep the hutches warm. Doors may drop forward to open or be on hinges in the normal way. Rabbits are clever little animals and can undo most fastenings or doors in order to escape! A hasp and staple is the safest closure. Hutches may be stacked in tiers of two or three, with an overhanging roof outside. The hutch measuring 1200 × 600 × 450 mm (4 ft. × 2 ft. × 18 in.) is suitable for breeding does and for rearing litters, but the bucks can be housed in hutches 900 × 600 × 450 mm (3 ft. × 2 ft. × 18 in.). Hutches may be bought ready made, but are easily made at home by a handyman from new or secondhand wood; that from demolition sites is good if it is free from rot or woodworm. Unless it is tongued and grooved, the back and sides, as well as the roof, must be covered in bitumen felt. Ready-made hutches are made of tongued and grooved wood

A hasp and staple is the safest form of fastening for hutches

Indoor three-tier breeding hutch with lift-out wire fronts, not as good as hinged doors

with a stout framework. Galvanised wire mesh used for floors should be 14 or 12 gauge, with a mesh of 19 × 19 mm ($\frac{3}{4}$ × $\frac{3}{4}$ in.), which allows droppings to fall through but does not harm the rabbits' feet. If tiered hutches are preferred, the floor of the bottom one should be at least 250 mm (10 in.) from the ground, while with single deck pens this height should be 450 mm (18 in.). Wooden shutters for protection should cover three-quarters of the wire front and slot into easy fittings on the side edges. Indoor hutches need not have the sloping roof but shutters should be ready for use in front of the breeding compartment.

Wire mesh pens can also be made at home, each pen being a unit on its own for ease of cleaning and movement. Wire pens should be laid out on the flat deck system and open at the tops. For ease in reaching the rabbits the pens should be wider than they are deep. They should be supported on a firm base, either angle iron, iron piping or similar material. The lid should overlap the front to enable a spring fastener to be attached. There are several types of metal clips for joining the wire sides etc., Alpha clips being very satisfactory.

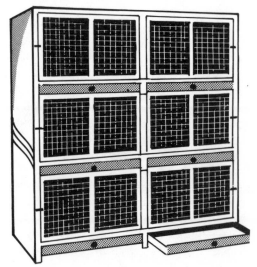

An excellent stock hutch for bucks or fattening young rabbits. Note the removable droppings trays, under wire-mesh floors

10

View of a commercial rabbit unit. Note the lights evenly spaced, the piping feeding the automatic water supply to each pen and the pellet hoppers. The record cards are pegged at the sides of the square hoppers. It is easy to see how tiers complicate the management, the lower tier needing a crouching position and the top one a very long arm or a step-stool for access

Equipment

The best equipment is very simple. Feedpots to be used inside a hutch need to be of heavy construction, of earthenware or galvanised steel, the latter should hang on the wire door. Heavy dog food pots are useful. In wire pens the feed hoppers hang outside the wire, with an opening through which the tray protrudes into the pen. Some feed hoppers are supplied with a wire sieve floor to enable the dust from the pellets to fall through rather than build up at the bottom of the hopper. Water containers are of several types.

In the larger unit with running water in the house, the nipple, automatic type is ideal. Otherwise use heavy earthenware pots in the hutch if they can be kept free from fouling. The best type is the bottle drinker, with a metal frame to hold a bottle outside the pen, and a small trough inside.

A hayrack saves waste, but in single-deck wire pens the hay can be put on the top of the pen so that the rabbits pull it down as they eat.

The need for strong equipment when it is sited inside the hutches becomes obvious when one sees a rabbit swing an earthenware pot around, and even bite a bit out of the rim! If the only kind available is too light, small moulds of concrete can be cast around the bowl or pot.

Earthenware pellet bowl with incurved rim to prevent pellets from being scratched out. These can be used for individual doses of medicine to a rabbit pen

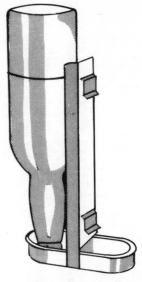

The most satisfactory type of bottle drinker, which takes ordinary squash bottles

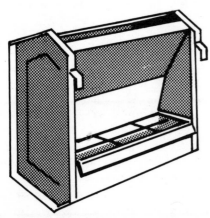

The ideal type of pellet hopper with wire grid to stop scratching and make it less cosy for the babies to sit in and foul the food! The feed tray is inserted through the wire and the hopper filled from outside, reducing the time and labour of feeding

Bottle drinker with tube mouthpiece. These are suspended outside hutches or pens with the mouthpiece through the wire

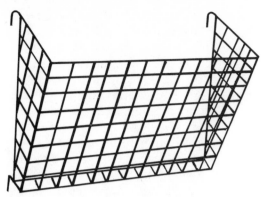

Wire hay rack which can be hooked on the outside of indoor pens or inside outdoor kinds. Its use keeps the hay unspoiled and prevents waste because the rabbits only pull as required

A nestbox will be needed for the wire pen, but the solid-floor hutch with its divided nesting compartment just requires plenty of soft meadow hay and for the shutter to be left in place. Nestboxes made of wood are the cheapest kind. They should be 500 × 250 mm (20 × 10 in.) with the back about 250 mm (10 in.) high sloping to the front height of 120 mm (5 in.). I prefer nestboxes without a lid; it is so much better for the doe to jump in and out without risking hurting her back, and also helps one keep a keen eye on the babies.

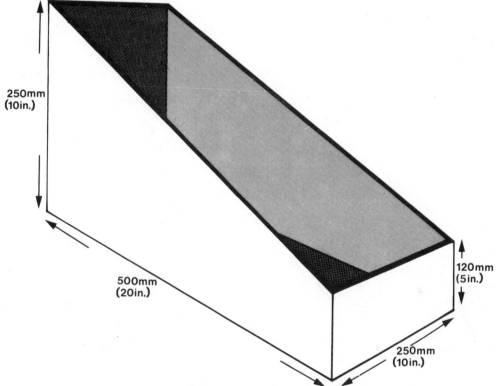

250mm (10in.)

500mm (20in.)

120mm (5in.)

250mm (10in.)

Nest box for use in wire pens. Wood is the best material; asbestos and plastics are too cold and are dangerous if the rabbits chew the edges. The rims can be painted with creosote after each disinfection if the rabbits are inclined to nibble them. The front of the box is lower to allow the heavily pregnant doe easy access without risk of injury to her milk glands etc., and to let the babies get back when they begin to come out to feed and explore

A scraper is needed to clean out the hutches and a bucket and wheelbarrow to remove the manure from the area. A brush for sweeping up is best kept specially for the task and I like to keep a can of creosote for daubing any woodwork the rabbits may nibble as well as painting out the hutches. Bedding must be supplied for the solid floors; white wood shavings are best and can often be obtained free for the fetching from timber merchants. Keep the shavings in dry, clean bags. Wire-mesh floors do not need bedding but some shavings can be added to the hay to help line the nestboxes. Sawdust is sometimes used but has a tendency to become sodden, and when dry it is liable to fly up into the rabbit's eyes and nose.

Useful scraper for clearing out droppings trays and hutches with solid floors

Storage of Foodstuffs and Hay

Rabbit feed pellets should be kept in the bags on racks in a dry place. The racks can be slats of wood or metal raising the bags sufficiently for air to circulate and to put it out of reach of rats or mice. Bales of hay can be stored similarly, especially if they are used as follows:

Cut one tie and remove enough hay to fill a bag or two, then retie the twine tightly. This will prevent hay from flying about and getting wasted. Green foods should be fresh and not stored. Roots should be stored in a dry place, free from frost and mould. Inspection for damage or moulds must be regularly undertaken. Grains such as oats should be stored in bags as for pellets.

A pair of scales with a scoop pan will be needed for weighing the young rabbits. A folded newspaper in the scoop saves the baby rabbits from a chilly shock.

All equipment should be the best possible combination of simplicity and efficiency. Expensive and complicated items will not give the service that can be expected from sturdier kinds. Everything must be easily cleaned and disinfected, smooth-surfaced and free from rough or sharp edges.

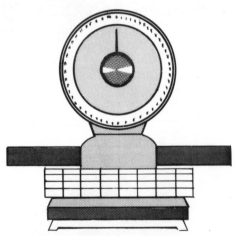

Practical scales, so essential in the rabbitry. Rabbit packers with European trade use metric scales, so if buying new scales, get those with both metric and imperial measures marked on them

Buying Your Stock

Breeds Suitable for Meat Production

With the exception of the wool-producing Angora and the tiny Polish and Netherland Dwarfs, all rabbit breeds can be used for meat, with varying success. The best ones are the New Zealand Whites and Californians, bred specifically for the task by commercial producers. If the home rabbit keeper has one of the show breeds he can still have some very good rabbits for the table, but production will be irregular and slower. Each carcase will have eaten more food and therefore be a little more expensive to produce. Rex breeds produce a very tender fine-grained meat but they are not very meaty until after about five months of age. The young rex rabbit has a greater proportion of bone to meat.

A good New Zealand White buck of the right meaty type and broad shoulders, with a short neck

Two views of a nice New Zealand White breeding doe. She has good conformation with plenty of room for a big litter to feed comfortably. A normal, but pronounced, dewlap can be seen under her chin

A good Californian buck with broad shoulders as well as hindquarters

Good New Zealand Whites and Californians produce fast growing litters of six to eight, just right to keep the family fed until the next litter is ready. The time from the day the doe is mated to the date the young rabbits are ready for killing is about a hundred days. Some new rabbit keepers may be led to believe that the giant breeds, such as Flemish Giant, will be better meat producers. They used to be so considered but with the coming of the modern strains of meat rabbits we realise how the old giants failed. Until it is about six months old the giant has comparatively little flesh on its large bones, and this factor, combined with a heavy hide to its pelt, means the resulting carcase is poor by normal standards. The flesh of the giant is coarser in fibre than that of the special meat strains and is therefore less appetising.

Sources of Reliable Stock

No one wants to waste money by buying unsuitable breeding stock however 'cheap' it may seem, so avoid pet shops and markets. The rabbits look fine but may not be capable of producing plenty of good meat rabbits. It is better to buy breeding does and bucks from a breeder accredited by the Commercial Rabbit Association, or from someone recommended by members of a branch of that Association or commercial Rabbit Group. Any of these suppliers will be interested in after-sales help and advice and be easily reached locally. Many of them will give a fourteen-day guarantee, replacing any rabbit that dies or becomes ill in that time.

Where possible it is better to buy from a larger herd rather than from someone with less than thirty or forty does, for there is less risk of the new herd's getting into difficulties from breeding close relatives among the stock. This leads to a quick deterioration in the health and stamina of the rabbits. Rabbits from small herds are also more likely to develop undesirable characteristics, due to close inbreeding.

Age to Buy

Adult rabbits, i.e. those over five months of age, do not like changes, so it is better to buy those of twelve to fourteen weeks of age. They will not mind the change so much and will have had a chance to settle happily in their new home before they need to be mated at about twenty weeks. It does mean that the rabbit keeper has to wait a little longer and with some patience for his tasty meals, but it is the only way to success. Adult rabbits, or those sold as 'mated', are often the source of endless trouble. It is also cheaper to buy the younger rabbits, even if you then use pellet feeds, which are admittedly rather expensive—but so much more efficient.

A word about mated does. These have been put to a buck, who apparently mated them successfully, but there is no guarantee that the doe is in kindle, so that to pay extra money for a 'mated' doe is really a waste of money. By buying younger stock the owner and the rabbits become better acquainted, and with frequent handling each develops confidence in the other.

I cannot stress too often the importance of handling rabbits, for a great deal of the difficulty in getting newly bought does properly into kindle is due to lack of handling. The owner is apprehensive lest the rabbit bite, scratch or get away; the rabbit feels insecure and may do all of them!

The correct way to hold a rabbit for inspection, supporting the hindquarters to save strain on the ears and neck

Number to Buy

This depends on three things:

1. The money available to buy the rabbits, to buy or make the hutches and to feed them until the first meat rabbits are ready for eating.
2. The time and space that can be spared for their care.
3. The number of rabbits wanted for the family and friends.

It is better to start with a few and then add more as one gains experience and as the market outlet grows when more and more friends and neighbours discover how delicious rabbit can be. A good doe will rear, under home conditions, about four to five litters a year, each of six to seven babies.

This makes a total of around thirty meat rabbits a year per doe. This is only a rough guide, as some does do better and there will always be a few missed matings in the course of a year.

Another point for consideration is the need for a buck to be kept reasonably busy. One buck and two to three does means that he is apt to get a bit fat and lazy. A good ratio is one buck to ten does, so it may be wise for several home rabbit breeders to combine and use one buck between them in that proportion of does. Great care should be taken that the rabbits are perfectly healthy before visiting or being visited for matings. A young buck from the third round of litters might be kept as a replacement in case of emergency, to save the expense of buying in another adult. Even if starting with a buck and two does only, do try to expand to ten does as experience is gained and the rabbit meat gets more popular in the district.

The number to be bought must also be related to the number of pens or hutches. Each doe will need an extra pen or hutch for the fattening of her litter while she is busy with the next one. The buck must also have his own hutch.

Recognising a Healthy Rabbit

A healthy rabbit has a sleek, shining coat, bright eyes, a dry clean nose and no discharge from eyes or nose. It has good fur on the hocks and is clean and dry around the vent and under the tail. It must have a well-covered backbone, for if the bones are easily felt along the back it may have coccidiosis.

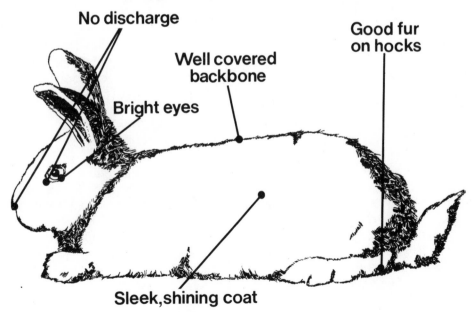

Recognising a Healthy Rabbit

No discharge

Good fur on hocks

Well covered backbone

Bright eyes

Sleek, shining coat

The Attributes of a Good Meat-producing Rabbit

1. Good health.
2. To have come from good stock with a history of good meat production.
3. To be well fleshed, broad across the shoulders and hindquarters with a short neck and wide loins.
4. To have light to medium bone structure and a good meat-to-bone ratio.
5. To have dense fur with some resistance, i.e. not too fine and soft.
6. The does to be roomy with eight visible, good teats.
7. The buck to be compact and meaty, and to remind one of a nice big Hereford bull!
8. The does to produce regularly and rear the young with plenty of milk.

Some of these points will only become obvious after a little time but they are all important. When buying rabbits for breeding the buyer should make an effort to visit the breeder's herd and ask to see the records. These should show plenty of litters from each doe and good weight-for-age figures. Before making any decision about the source of stock, remember that if any economies have to be made to meet financial limits, let them be made in hutches, etc. Make at home rather than buy ready-made, but try not to skimp on the stock. Equipment can always be improved, but buying poor breeding stock sets the enterprise on the way to failure at once. A little extra on the cost of the rabbits, given that the source is reliable, will save pounds in the long run.

Simple Records

In order to avoid muddles and too much inbreeding a few simple records must be kept. A piece of stiff cardboard, 180 × 120 mm (7 × 5 in.) can be ruled off, making it a matter of seconds to fill in the daily notes.

One card should be kept for the buck with records of his matings and the resulting litters. Another card should be kept for each doe, with more detail about the litters. Do enter in the 'comment' column any odd happenings, however trivial. They may make all the difference to tracing back the origin of any trouble that may occur in the future.

A record should also be kept of the quantity and cost of all foodstuffs bought for the rabbits, and also of the weights and ages of all rabbits killed for meat. Even if no money changes hands when the meat is for the family, chart the current price which would have been paid in a shop for it. This helps to show what the meat is costing the keeper. Many rabbit keepers find that a desk diary with a pencil attached firmly to it will help them keep those records up to date! Good records join with good stock and good management in making for success in rabbit keeping, whether in a small home unit or a large commercial one.

Some Breeds of Rabbit

There are nearly fifty different breeds of domestic rabbits, if one counts the various colours and patterns separately, but there are only four main divisions described by the type of fur they bear. We see normal fur, rex fur, satin fur and one quite on its own, the wool-bearing Angora. There are other gradings, with self-coloured, patterned or

RECORD CARDS

DOE RECORD CARD							Date of Birth

Hutch No. _____   Sire _____   Dam _____ _____

Date Mated	Buck	Date Kindled	No. Born	No. Reared	Litter Weight 3 weeks	Litter Weight 8 weeks	Comments

BUCK RECORD CARD					Date of Birth

Hutch No. _____   Sire _____   Dam _____ _____

Date Mated	Doe	Litter Born	Number in Litter	Number Reared	Comments

shaded coats and they come in many shapes and sizes, from the tiny Netherland Dwarf to the Giants. The Himalayan is slim and snakey, the Beveren mandolin-shaped, the Dutch very compact while the Lop has enormous ears, spreading over 500 mm (20 in.) or more.

21

Breeds Best for Meat Production

A good meat rabbit should carry plenty of meat on its forequarters as well as hindquarters, otherwise one has a bony forequarter with very little meat on it. The meat breed has to have a fast growth rate to put on meat at the earliest age possible, so that when it reaches a live weight of 2–2.5 kg ($4\frac{1}{2}$–$5\frac{1}{2}$ lb.) it will have a carcase weight of 1–1.25 kg ($2\frac{1}{4}$–$2\frac{3}{4}$ lb.), just right for a family meal. In order to carry the meat the rabbit must have an adult live weight of about 5.5 kg (12 lb.) for does and 5 kg (11 lb.) for bucks. There are several breeds in this range but very few have been developed for good meat production. While the Show emphasis lies in the external beauties, the meat points or inner characteristics of growth rate, meat-to-bone ratio, conformation and food conversion ratios are apt to be overlooked. Two meat breeds have been developed and are available in this country, the Californian and the New Zealand White. Other breeds are capable of up-grading with comparatively little trouble including most of those of about 4 kg (9 lb.) live adult weight, plus one or two a little smaller. The Argente Champagne, Beveren, Chinchilla Giganta, English, New Zealand Red, the larger Rex strains and some Satins show some potential for development. I have not included those two large breeds, the Belgian Hare, and Flemish Giant, for their meat-to-bone ratio and growth rates are not suitable for modern meat demands.

The Californian. A white rabbit with black or dark brown ears, nose, tail and feet. Adult weights are about 4.5 kg (10 lb.) for bucks and 5 kg (11 lb.) for does. Fur is dense and close, and they have medium bone, broad shoulders and hindquarters, and placid temperament.

New Zealand White. White rabbit with pink eyes. Adult bucks weigh about 5 kg (11 lb.), does about 5.5 kg (12 lb.). Fur is dense and longer than the Californian's. Bucks are compact but does are longer in body and have more room for suckling large litters.

Argente Champagne. Silvery-coloured fur, adult weight about 4 kg (9 lb.). Good hindquarters but needs upgrading for shoulder breadth.

Beveren. White, blue, black or brown. Good hindquarters, mandolin-shaped. Adults 3.5 kg (8 lb.) plus.

Chinchilla Giganta. This is a breed produced for meat from the normal sized Chinchilla rabbit, but its coloured coat has precluded it from full development as a meat producer for the market demand. It has a heavy coat with attractive markings, a meaty body and a weight range rather like the New Zealand White.

English. A patterned rabbit with coloured markings on a white ground. Good flesh and medium bone, adults about 3.5 kg (8 lb).

New Zealand Red. If the processors had not been so adamant about having a basically white fur on their meat rabbits, the Red could have taken its place among the meat breeds, with only growth rates and other inner factors to be up-graded. Adult bucks 5 kg (11 lb.), does 5.5 kg (12 lb.).

The Rex Breeds. These vary considerably in size but the meat is especially fine in texture and of superb flavour. There are a number of colours in Rex coats, which make excellent hard-wearing garments and have a delightful soft velvety feel. Being short and dense it wears well with less tendency to shedding hairs in use. The larger Rex rabbit breeds have an adult weight of about 4 kg (9 lb.) with medium bone.

Satins. The fur is long, very fine and silky with a sheen which goes right down the hairs. The adult weight varies with the type of rabbit, depending on which breed has the satin coat bred into it, some being quite meaty.

Belgian Hare. This is a true rabbit in spite of its name, which refers to its type and stance rather than its ancestors! In the past this was held in great esteem for meat but it requires a large hutch, and is rather slim built for a good meat type. Adult weights about 4–4.5 kg (9–10 lb.).

Flemish Giant. This used to be the meat breed but it is far too heavy in bone, and as it does not put on flesh until its bone framework is developed, it becomes meaty later than other breeds. It also requires a lot of room and has rather a poor food conversion ratio, i.e. needs more food than most breeds to produce a kilogramme of meat. The meat is coarser in grain than that of other breeds.

Breeds Less Important for Meat Production

The other Argente colours, Chinchilla, Dutch, Fox, Havana, Lilac, Sables, Siberian, Silver and Smoke Pearl. Of these the Dutch and Chinchilla are often used for home meat production as a smaller carcase for smaller families, and as a by-product of the breed's being kept for show purposes.

The other Argentes. These are smaller than the Champagne, but fairly cobby. The young rabbits would not be as meaty as in a larger breed even if they had a fast growth rate.

Chinchilla. Between the wars these were very popular for meat. Its adult weight is about 3 kg ($6\frac{1}{2}$ lb.) with fine bone and good flesh texture.

Dutch. There are several colours, but the pattern is distinctive and well known. The 'little Dutch' as it is affectionately known, matures early, matching the meat breeds, but being a small breed of a maximum weight of 2.5 kg ($5\frac{1}{2}$ lb.) it is not so suitable for meat. It is cobby and meaty for its size however.

The other breeds listed are medium in size and of about 3 kg ($6\frac{1}{2}$ lb.) adult weight, and have never been developed as meat breeds. The young adults all make useful table rabbits.

Breeds Unsuitable for Meat Production

The Angora heads this list as it produces a poor carcase, whatever its size. The tiny breeds, Netherland Dwarf, Polish and the snakey Himalayan, as well as the small Tan, have obviously little meat potential.

Angora. This is a unique breed of rabbit, in several colours and white. The fur is very long, fine, about 120 mm (5 in.) in length. It is known as wool and is plucked from the live rabbit and spun, instead of the skin being taken from a dead rabbit. The Angora gives an impression of being a large rabbit of a snowball type, but the body is rather slim and not suitable for meat production. It is a breed which needs highly specialised and time-consuming care.

Netherland Dwarf. As its name implies is a tiny rabbit of many colours and types of coat. The adult weight is 1 kg ($2\frac{1}{4}$ lb.).

Polish. Like the Dwarf this has a top weight of around 1 kg ($2\frac{1}{4}$ lb.).

Himalayan. This is a snakey type with a top weight of about 2.5 kg ($5\frac{1}{2}$ lb.) but not much meat on the bones.

Tan. A breed which has a weight of about 2 kg ($4\frac{1}{2}$ lb.) but is not as cobby as a Dutch.

Several Continental breeds have been introduced into this country but results are as varied as the strains from which they come. Many of the imported breeds are still primarily show rabbits, or used to supply the Continental demand for very large adult rabbits for meat. This is not what our market demands. We prefer a smaller, younger and more tender rabbit. Keeping rabbits until very large and mature means a much heavier food bill, and more hutches or pens.

With so many different breeds to choose from, it is small wonder that the new rabbit keeper is bewildered. However, if he keeps to the well-tried meat breeds he will have good meals for the family at the least expense. As a rough estimate taken from records of an average herd, in 1978 it costs about 1.5p per day from birth to killing to feed a rabbit for meat. This is using a feed cost of about £115 per ton and meat prices at 33p per live weight of 0.5 kg (18 oz.). The profit per meat rabbit could be between 30p and 45p, making a reasonable joint for lunch!

How to Feed Rabbits

Basic Nutritional Needs

The secret of successful feeding of rabbits lies in getting a well-balanced diet containing all the necessary ingredients in the correct proportions and in a palatable form. This has already been done by the compounder in the case of pelleted feeds, and the rabbit keeper has only to add hay and water to get the best results. Each ingredient has been checked for nutrition, suitability and good condition, taking the worry and hard work out of rabbit feeding. If the rabbits are to be fed on a mixed, or home-gathered diet the owner needs to know something of the rabbit's digestive system and of the values of the various foodstuffs. The rabbit must have some of each of the following items:

1. Proteins which are body builders, found in grains such as oats, good hay and to a certain extent in green foods.
2. Starchy foods for heat and energy, found in similar articles of food.
3. Fibrous material for good digestion and as a balancer for the other goods. Hay is the best source of this material.
4. Vitamins A, D and E are essential for rabbits, while they seem to control their supply of vitamin B and its associates. Vitamin C does not seem to be so essential to rabbits.
5. Minerals. The home rabbit keeper will find that the mineral balance usually works out satisfactorily, unless the foods are of poor quality or condition, or the soils on which they are grown are gravely deficient in any of the minerals.
6. Fresh drinking water is very important, whatever the type of feeding employed.

The rabbit's digestive organs are so arranged that it needs to be able to nibble most of the twenty-four hours, relying on the presence of a bulky mass of food in the stomach to ensure its passage through the system. This means that the rabbit can take quite a bit of hay, but it has been found that it is not wise to rely on green foods or roots for the bulk. Otherwise side effects will be encountered. The pelleted feeds are carefully checked for their content down to the tiniest amount of mineral or vitamin, and thus a constant level of nutrition is maintained.

The home rabbit keeper who is going to feed his own mixed diet has problems in deciding the food value of his diet. This varies in the roots and greens with the age of the crop when harvested, the soil it is grown in, and the weather during all its stages. This makes it even more important to give a good mixture of different kinds of greens so that one may make good the deficiencies or excesses of another item. It must be recalled that a combination of pellets and a mixed diet is not the complete answer to a cheaper feeding routine. The fact that the pellets are formulated as a complete food in themselves will result in a dilution of the feed value when mixed with anything but hay. A good basic mixed diet should include oats (the best of the grains), greens or roots according to whether it is summer or winter, hay and water. Some of the grain can be varied with chunks of stale brown bread which have been dried hard in a slow oven.

The Importance of Hay

This is an important item in the rabbits' diet supplying the fibre they need, giving them something at which to nibble at all times, as well as balancing the diet. Good meadow hay is the best, true clover hay is too coarse and of doubtful feed value and leads to possible digestive upsets. Hay made from well-grown stinging nettles, cut when fresh and green and dried carefully makes a pleasant change for the rabbits, and is very rich in protein. All hay should be free from dust and moulds, and should not contain any very coarse or poisonous weeds. Well-made hay smells sweet, with no mustiness, and has a faint tang of the nicest tobacco. When the peacrop has finished, the haulm can be cut and dried and will be relished by the rabbits.

There is one warning about hay that is sometimes overlooked. New season's hay, i.e cut within the last three to four months, will often scour the rabbits. The hay needs to mature before being fed. Some pellet manufacturers state that hay is not necessary with their brand of pellets, but I always advise its use. A small amount is neither expensive nor troublesome, but it does give a safeguard against digestive upsets from too rich a diet. If there is a shortage of hay the rabbits can have oat straw, but it is not as satisfactory in practical use.

The Supply of Drinking Water

It is surprising how often we still hear people say that hutch-bred rabbits do not need drinking water if they are fed greens. This fallacy leads to great suffering by the rabbits who have no water to drink. Clean fresh water should always be available, preferably supplied in bottle drinkers if an automatic nipple valve system is impossible. Many small units will not have running water laid to their rabbitry, so that an automatic system is impossible. In very cold weather the water should be given luke-warm when the rabbits will enjoy a drink. They will drink ice cold water if they **have** to do so, but it may cause chill or digestive upsets.

Before using well or stream water in a country rabbitry have it analysed for safety. It may contain pollution of various kinds. Water fit for humans to drink is water fit for rabbits! Rabbits fed on pellets and hay with little or no greens will drink a lot of water in a day, varying slightly between cold and hot weather and of course the ages of the stock. The baby with plenty of doe's milk has no business to be attempting to drink water. An adult doe such as a Californian will drink 0.25 litre ($\frac{1}{2}$ pt.) in twenty-four hours. A doe with a litter of seven to eight at three weeks of age needs 0.5–0.625 litre (1–1$\frac{1}{4}$ pt.). A litter of seven to eight in a hutch together at eight weeks may drink as much as 1.5 litre (2$\frac{1}{2}$ pt.). Baby rabbits start to drink water and eat the solid food provided as soon as they come out of the nest.

Intensive Feeding

This is the method used to cut down work by feeding once a day, to ensure that the rabbits get a balanced diet and to produce the best type of prime meat rabbit. It will cost more in hard cash than the extensive method but the returns will be correspondingly higher. The food is compounded by the miller into pellets, each pellet being 4 mm ($\frac{1}{6}$ in.) in diameter and 10 mm ($\frac{2}{5}$ in.) in length. They are hard and may be green or greenish-brown in colour, depending on the ingredients used. The pellets contain balanced quantities of all the nutriments required by the rabbit from birth to death, and during breeding. Some experiments have been made to find a cheaper pellet for fattening the weaners. The rabbit is so resistant to change of any kind in its life that it was apt to suffer a setback when the food was changed. Most suppliers now make one pellet. It is so cleverly formulated that it can be used in smaller amounts for the maintenance of the adult rabbit, and also for the needs of the pregnant and milking doe as well as to fatten the meat rabbits.

Extensive Feeding

The rabbit keeper enters a more complicated area of rabbit feeding when he decides to use the extensive method of feeding. This entails the purchase of pellets or grain such as oats, hay and whatever roots are not grown in the garden. Water is still supplied. The roots or green foods have to be harvested or collected. The rabbit should be fed twice a day, one feed being of grain or dried bread, the other of greens or roots; hay is given once a day. Rabbits will often leave the husks of the whole oats, which are the best buy and these husks must be emptied from the pots or hoppers regularly. Crushed oats are extravagant, for the kernel or 'meal' is too often lost as powder, and the rabbits will not eat dusty foods as it makes them sneeze and irritates their eyes. Always remove left-over foods, for they are a sign that either there was too much for the rabbit's appetite, or that the food has been fouled. Adjust the quantities accordingly.

Green Foods

The list of green foods suitable for rabbits is very long. We will just mention a few, and the general principles apply for them all. Always feed greens fresh, and if they need to lie around for a few hours, spread them out. Heaped greens soon ferment and can kill young rabbits. Fresh cut grass is the best green food for rabbits, but not as lawn mowings. These heat in such a short time that the rabbit has hardly time to eat them. Wilted greens will not hurt as long as they are not yellowing. Of the garden crops rabbits can have chicory leaves, kohl rabi, carrot leaves and the leaves of the cabbage family. The latter should be given in smaller amounts as they tend to be very strong.

Wild plants in common use include hedge parsley, dandelion, coltsfoot leaves, sow thistle, plantain and knapweed.

Plants to avoid are all those with bulbous roots such as buttercups and daffodils, as well as ivy berries, laburnam, etc. Several plants have value as medicines for rabbits. At the first sign of scours give shepherd's purse, blackberry, raspberry or strawberry leaves. Too much dandelion will cause a condition called red water, leading, if persisted in, to kidney troubles. Too much cabbage will result in a lot of urine being passed with a strong unpleasant smell in the hutch.

Four very useful garden plants

Kohl Rabi   Rabbits enjoy the leaves and the 'bulb' if it can be spared from the producer's table. The flavour is delicious and delicately 'turnip'. It should be used for the table when the bulb is the size of a cricket ball

Carrots   The leaves from summer pullings and the roots in winter are very good for rabbits. Carrot roots have a higher food content than swedes or mangolds, the latter having a high water level

Cabbage   Feed all members of the cabbage family sparingly to rabbits, as excess may cause urinary troubles and a smell in the rabbit house

Chicory   The leaves are picked from the outside of the plant which will then continue to bear successive crops

Raspberry, blackberry and strawberry leaves   These are equal in value to the shepherd's purse for the early treatment of scours. Rabbits will often eat one of these leaves when all other food is refused

Useful wild plants. The leaves are used before the flowers open. After then the leaves may be too coarse for easy digestion and will certainly have lost a lot of the food value. Coltsfoot is the sole exception, for its flowers come long before the leaves. All wild plants are best fed in as wide a variety as possible.

Plantain   The narrow or broad leaved species should be used before flowering

Dandelion   Feed sparingly as it can cause red water

Shepherd's Purse This is so called from the shape of the seed pods. Very useful as medicinal herb if given early to cases of suspected scours

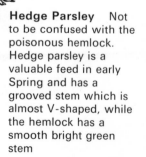

Hedge Parsley   Not to be confused with the poisonous hemlock. Hedge parsley is a valuable feed in early Spring and has a grooved stem which is almost V-shaped, while the hemlock has a smooth bright green stem

Coltsfoot   The leaves are a useful addition to a mixed feed for rabbits

Knapweed   It is slightly astringent and so is less likely to cause scours

Sow thistle   Very valuable for nursing does and well liked by them

Grass   Grass is the one greenfood which never scours a rabbit if it is fed properly, freshly cut and not frosted or mouldy

Roots

Roots suitable for rabbit food include carrots, swedes and mangolds. The carrot is the most valuable in nutrition, while the swede and mangold contain a high percentage of water. Mangolds should not be fed until after Christmas, as they need to mature in store, otherwise they may cause scours. Sugar beet can be fed to fatteners for meat, but never to breeding stock or those being reared as possible breeding stock. It makes them far too fat and sterile.

The Use of Green Foods and Roots

Never give frosted or thawed out foods of any kind, and avoid mouldy or rotting foods. Be sure that no fertiliser, weed-killer or insecticide has been sprayed on any plants picked for feeding rabbits. Also to be avoided are areas contaminated by cats or dogs. Roadside verges used to be very popular sources of greens, but nowadays they are too polluted due to diesel and petrol fumes as well as spraying by the authorities. Greens from gardens and allotments are the safest for our rabbits.

Amounts to Feed

Different types of rabbits, different ages and working types need different rations. For adult rabbits such as bucks and does that are not in kindle or milking 112 g (4 oz.) of pellets are sufficient, unless they show a definite need for a little more to keep them in condition. Does in kindle need to have their rations increased so that during the last ten days before kindling she reaches 224 g (8 oz.). From the day she kindles until the litter is weaned at twenty-one to twenty-eight days, the amount must be increased with the increasing appetites of the youngsters. It may be to a total of 0.5–0.75 kg (18 oz.–1¾ lb.). After weaning and a few days of small rations, the rabbits may be 'fed to appetite'. This means that they have just enough each day to leave only a pellet or so when feeding time comes round again. At eight weeks of age or at market weight when the meat rabbits go to market, the young rabbits kept for breeding must have the daily ration reduced to the 112 g (4 oz.). Again this may be increased a little if they seem to need it.

It is almost impossible to give definite amounts for green foods as they vary so much in bulk and weight. As with pellets, the golden rule is to give only the amount that is consumed before the next feed. In the case of greens and roots, the surplus should be removed when the next feed is offered. It is better to err a little on the mean side, for as long as there is hay in the rack or on top of the pen the rabbits will not come to any harm over a short period. The average adult rabbit can eat a piece of root the size of a cricket ball, and it is better to give a lump rather than slices or little bits.

In hot weather it will be noticed that the rabbits tend to eat more at night when it is cooler. This is quite normal.

Good Management

Stress

Good management covers the whole field of keeping the rabbits in suitable surroundings, looking after their health and feeding, as well as many other aspects. Perhaps the most important of these is the prevention of stresses caused by adverse influences on the rabbits' lives. A rabbit in a state of stress is unable to rest comfortably, to eat with good appetite or to digest what it does manage to eat, and it is very liable to contract illnesses and infections. Stress is a condition of tension and lowered vitality caused by many factors including fright, unsuitable hutch or pen, errors of feeding, unusual noise, disturbance by cats, dogs or vermin, and even by strangers visiting the unit. A certain amount of stress results quite naturally from the normal changes of its life, from weaning, changes of diet, mating, kindling or even being weighed. Prevention is much better than attempted cures, so that the management of the rabbitry should be so planned that it prevents stress from external causes and reduces the severity of stress due to natural causes. It cannot be entirely eliminated from the rabbit's life. A newly weaned rabbit is under some strain, but this need not be made worse by putting it into a cold hutch, or making changes in its diet while it is adjusting to the loss of the doe's warmth and milk.

The Importance of Hygiene

Keeping the rabbitry clean is one of the most important tasks and a strict routine should be kept. Dust, cobwebs, fluff and rabbit fur all provide happy homes for germs. Piles of mouldy hay, foodstuffs or wet droppings will encourage smells, vermin and disease. Rabbits will not thrive if they are kept in messy surroundings. A stuffy atmosphere is fatal to rabbits and so is disease resulting from flies and dirt. Keep the rabbitry, whether indoors or outside, swept clean and tidy.

Cleaning Out

At regular intervals wash down walls and ledges with a wet mop or brush. Dry dusting or wiping will only raise a dust which will settle in another patch. Keep windows and light bulbs clean to ensure the maximum of light in the house. Wash down concrete floors, but do not leave puddles of wet to make the place too humid.

Whenever a pen or hutch is emptied of its occupant, scrape off all dirt and droppings, wash the pen out with a good detergent, then with a disinfectant like Jeyes, and dry well. If wooden hutches need it, give them a coating of creosote and allow this to dry before putting another rabbit in. It is necessary to wash with detergent first, because many disinfectants will not work properly in the presence of animal droppings or urine. Solid-floor hutches should be cleaned out weekly, and a handful of bedding (shavings) put on the dirty patch each morning. Wire pens do not need cleaning, but if the droppings fall on to a tray just under the floor, this may need emptying daily or every few days. If not watched, the droppings pile up and clog the floor mesh. If the droppings from a wire pen fall to the ground beneath, it is still necessary to keep to a regular interval of cleaning out, the interval depending on the state of the ground, etc. A layer of shavings under the pens will help to absorb the urine and keep the rabbitry sweeter. If the hutches are out of doors a cement or brick path makes both keeping the feet dry and sweeping up easier.

If there has been any illness among the rabbits be sure to clean and disinfect the hutches or pens very thoroughly, and if at all possible, put them out in the sun to sweeten. Creosote in wooden hutches is a wonderful disinfectant. When cleaning hutches or pens check that the fastenings for door or top opening are working properly.

Cleaning Equipment

This includes feed and water containers, which should be washed regularly in hot detergent and rinsed thoroughly afterwards. Spades, brooms and scrapers used for hutch cleaning, etc., should be put into a bucket of disinfectant once a week for an hour or so. Then they should be dried in the air. Wash the pan of the scales after weighing the rabbits. Nestboxes should be scrubbed and disinfected after every litter and dried in the open air when possible. Special care should be given to the nesting area in hutches after the litter has been weaned. Neglect of these precautions can lead to a chain of infection being passed from litter to litter, each time the trouble becoming stronger and less easy to control.

Artificial Lighting

Rabbits naturally slow down their breeding processes when the hours of daylight shorten, and only speed up again with the lengthening in the Spring. If kept under good management home-bred rabbits will breed all the year round, and of course there is no close season for the meat. In order to give them every help, the rabbit house or shed should have some artificial lighting during the shorter days. If the does can be given fourteen to sixteen hours of light, daylight plus artificial, they are more likely to breed steadily through the winter. 40-watt lamps at intervals of 3 m (10 ft.) one way and 6 m (20 ft.) the other, with a height of 2.5 m (8 ft.) above the ground level will give sufficient light. The bucks should not be placed directly under a light bulb. Even greater economy in running costs can be made by the use of fluorescent fittings, although the cost of installation is higher than with the socket and bulb type. The light is diffused more evenly and lower wattage gives a brighter light. The fittings may be spaced at larger intervals, so fewer are required.

Avoiding Waste

Waste and forgetfulness of any kind is expensive, be it waste of food, forgetfulness of kindling dates and nestbox dates, or waste of time walking up and down the pens when an alley at the end would cut the journeys by half. Do not overfill feed containers, give only moderate amounts of hay, use racks or the tops of the pens so that the hay is drawn down as needed.

Killing

Before slaughter, a rabbit should be starved of food overnight or if it is to be killed in the evening, for the whole day. Leave a little water for it to drink. The digestive tract will have emptied itself during the fast, making the dressing of the carcase almost odourless. The water will prevent its becoming de-hydrated and the flesh tougher. Whether given water or not, the bladder will usually be found to have some urine in it.

The actual killing can be quite simple and cause no distress to the rabbit. The selected rabbit is placed on the edge of a table, the back legs grasped in one hand. The right hand slides up the back to just behind the ears. The grasp is tightened; a quick drop of the right hand towards the floor, stretch and twist and the neck is broken, without even a squeak from the rabbit. An alternative method of killing is to sit the rabbit on the edge of a table holding the ears over the face with one hand. Using a thick, stout stick the operator gives the rabbit a sharp blow on the back of the neck, breaking it. It is not as satisfactory a method as the first as it causes bruising of the neck meat and it is possible that the blow will misfire.

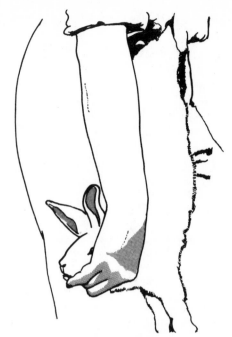

The best method of killing a rabbit, by pulling and twisting its neck. It is quick, effective and the rabbit never even squeals if it is done quickly and well

Dressing the Rabbit

Immediately after killing, hang the rabbit by the hind legs on two hooks at a convenient height. Cut off the head and allow the blood to drain into a large bowl. Skin at once, slitting the fur around the hocks and down the legs to the vent. Roll the skin off to the shoulders and push out the forelegs, cutting off at the knee joints.

The skin may be air dried on a wire stretcher, fur side inwards. See that the skin is stretched well down the wire and nip with clothes pegs to keep it stretched. Hang in a dry, airy place until quite dry. Dust the dry skin with Gammexane to keep it free from insects and store it in an airtight tin until needed.

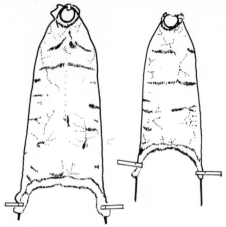

Skins or wire stretchers, sleeve-wise for air drying. The skins should be stretched smoothly and held with clothes pegs, or they will wrinkle during drying

Slit the belly of the carcase from vent to neck, taking care not to cut too deep and so puncture the entrails. Remove the entrails taking care not to let the bladder drain on the flesh and not to break the gall bladder, found under the liver. Cut it out carefully and save the liver, heart and kidneys in a separate dish, and put into the refrigerator to cool. The carcase may be left whole and stretched out, cut into joints or curled ready for stuffing and roasting. To do this, bend the rabbit, while still warm, with the feet in towards the belly. Place the front feet between the back ones and truss with string. This gives an attractive rounded joint.

Slitting the belly skin of a rabbit carcase, taking care not to puncture the internal organs while doing so

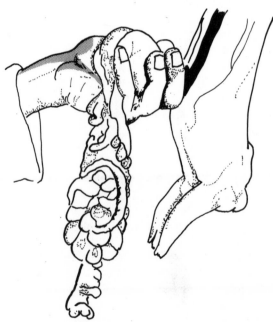

Removing the entrails complete with stomach and liver. Again, care is taken to avoid puncturing the gall bladder found in the folds of the liver

Carcases on a packing station production line. That on the right is of very much better quality than its neighbour

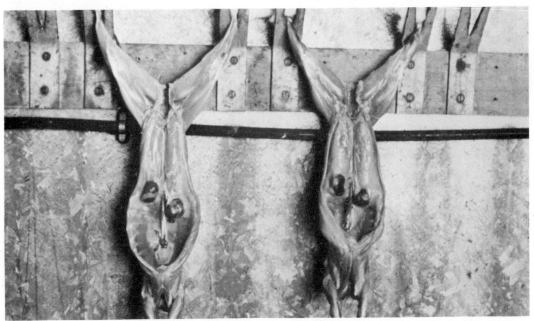

The same carcases after removal of the entrails, with the kidneys left in position. Note the pads of meat on either side of the spine of the prime carcase, an extra bonus in a well-fed and well-reared rabbit

Rabbit meat, jointed and packed on trays. The right-hand tray shows the more expensive selected hind legs, the others mixed joints

Storage of Rabbit Meat

Rabbit meat may be kept for several days in the domestic refrigerator, and it can also be stored in a deep freeze. Unless the carcase is very small it is better to joint it for deep freezing. Wrap each portion in a separate bag or paper wrapping, taking care to exclude the air, and seal carefully. Follow the instructions with your freezer as to freezing time and packing. Date each package before freezing and take care that no bones are allowed to puncture the packaging.

The Use of Pelts

The pelts from young home-bred rabbits killed for meat will probably be too frail and moulty for use, but those from rabbits of $4\frac{1}{2}$ months or aged six to nine months can be moult-free, and used for gloves, garments, trimmings, toys and children's slippers or pram covers. Every effort should be made to match pelts when more than one is used in an item. The colour, softness and thickness of the fur must be taken into account.

The pelts can be dried flat, if slit down the belly and tacked on to a board or behind a door in an airy cupboard. The fur should be against the board and surplus fat carefully scraped from shoulders, etc. Do not dry pelts close to direct heat or they will become brittle and will not cure properly.

If a prime pelt is required it is best taken from a rabbit of six to nine months when not in moult, and between the months of October and March. This will be the winter coat and the first adult coat, always the best coat the rabbit ever grows. Moult is a natural process when the rabbit sheds one coat and grows another.

The young can be caught for a short period free from moult at about ten to twelve weeks of age, at about $4\frac{1}{2}$ months as well as between six and nine months. After then the adult

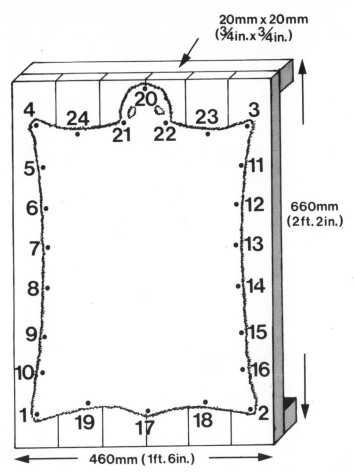

20mm x 20mm
(¾in. x ¾in.)

660mm
(2ft. 2in.)

460mm (1ft. 6in.)

Rabbit skin pinned on a board, fur side down for air drying. This is an alternative to sleeve drying in wire stretchers. Care must be taken not to overstretch the skin or it will have thin patches when dressed

rabbit usually has one big moult a year, often in late summer or early autumn. In breeds with coloured fur, moult can be seen on the underside of the pelt as a blue-black shadow. Living rabbits will show loose fur and new fur growing underneath. White-furred rabbits do not show such clear signs of moult.

Dressing the Pelts

This is the process which turns them from hard 'boards' into soft glossy furs, and puts a final gloss on the skins. Very few firms undertake to dress small numbers of skins, and when they do, it is very expensive. It is rather a difficult process for the amateur but it can be done. There are several methods and materials for the process, which consists of soaking the skins to soften them, getting rid of grease, pickling them and then oiling to produce the required suppleness. The skin will then be dried.

Rabbit Manure

The home-bred rabbit provides more than one useful product, for as well as meat and pelt the manure from the hutches is very valuable. No gardener need buy expensive artificial fertilisers if he uses his rabbit manure properly. It can be dug straight into the ground or composted and used as required at any time in the year. Equal layers of rabbit droppings and bedding with vegetable waste from the garden make an extra rich manure. This will feed the crops and also leave the soil in good heart. One little warning: Do not put manure containing weed seeds or hay bits on to the top of the soil. The seeds will germinate and be a great nuisance, so compost it or dig it in.

It is surprising how popular a rabbit keeper becomes when his friends see the crops he gets by using rabbit manure! Meat and vegetables at no extra cost! The quantity of manure from each rabbit will vary according to its body weight and the diet, plus the absence or presence of hutch bedding. An average adult rabbit will produce about 0.09 cu. m (3 cu. ft.) per year of droppings plus bedding and hay scraps. The weight of the manure varies with the amount of moisture in it: The wetter, the heavier. Rabbit manure is so valuable for crop production and soil conservation that one producer stated that he would keep rabbits for the manure alone, even if he were not making a profit from the meat. His market garden is maintained by rabbit manure.

Claw Clipping

Good management includes the care of the rabbit itself. If the claws are allowed to grow too long the rabbit can injure itself or others by scratching and will also walk awkwardly. Long claws will cause the foot to turn backwards with resulting sore hocks, and in the front feet, sore pads. In fact the discomfort of long claws can upset the breeding programme, for the buck may injure his doe at mating, the doe may be so uncomfortable that she will not mate, or will not look after her litter. In Nature, the wild rabbit keeps its claws short by scratching; the hutch- or pen-bred rabbit cannot do this and needs help from humans. A pinkish core will be seen in the nail; this is the quick or live part. Holding the fur out of the way, clip the claw back to within 3–4 mm ($\frac{1}{8}$–$\frac{1}{6}$ in.) of the quick. A pair of heavy nail clippers or side cutting pliers may be used.

Cleaning Soiled Fur

Should the rabbit's fur become soiled it can be cleaned by rubbing in some cornflour. Leave for a few moments and then groom out with the hands. This means rubbing the palms of the hands up and down the fur in long, smooth strokes. If the stain is very obstinate leave some cornflour in the fur for the rabbit to lick out. Matted fur around the vent or under the chin should be clipped off and the area wiped with damp cotton wool. Dry thoroughly.

Identifying the Rabbits

If there are fewer than five does in the rabbitry it may not be necessary to label the rabbits, especially if they are always kept in the same hutches. If there are over five does they must be numbered. This can be done by buying the leg rings issued by the British

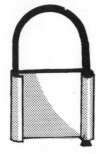

Marking Rabbits. Ear tags are sometimes used but can be torn out and cause the rabbit pain

Tattooing a rabbit's ear. The best tattoo forceps have a quick release spring action

Rabbit Council for the pure breeds, by tattooing the ears or by ear tags. The rings do not always fit the commercial types, even of the pure breeds, and the ear tags tend to get torn off, with a nasty wound left behind. Tattooing is by far the best method, using a special forceps and interchangeable numbers and letters. The code letters and numbers are imprinted inside the rabbit's ear flaps. It is only necessary to mark the breeding stock.

Breeding Rabbits

Breeding rabbits is both interesting and comparatively simple, for the doe is quite capable of attending to each stage of kindling by herself, and, indeed, prefers to be left alone and quiet at that time. If her hutch or pen is comfortable and she has access to clean drinking water she will cover her nest with her own belly fur and clear up the afterbirth. Some maiden does do make mistakes over their first litter, but this is sometimes due to the fact that they were mated too soon, before they were old enough or mature. Sometimes it can be due to disturbance or to stress from some reason. The second litter is usually born and reared with no further trouble.

Age to Mate

In the breeds most commonly used for meat production, the New Zealand White and the Californian, the does mature at about twenty weeks of age and may be mated then. The bucks need to be a little older as they mature more slowly, at about twenty-four weeks. A healthy doe will often show some redness and moisture around the vent area when she is ready for mating, but it is not necessary to wait for this sign. The bucks get restless when they are ready and may splash the walls of their hutches, or passers-by, with their semen.

Mating

Always take the doe to the buck, carrying her comfortably so that she arrives in a relaxed condition. If the stock has been well handled from birth or arrival in the unit, they will not resent the handling necessary for mating. Place the doe tail first in the buck's hutch or pen and either let her run around with the buck or assist her as follows.

Hold the doe by the scruff of her neck with her back to the buck. With the other hand under her belly, gently lift the tail end so that she is slightly raised towards the buck. If he is ready he will mount her, mate and fall off, sometimes with a small cry. If they are left to run and they do not mate within a reasonable time, remove the doe and bring her back to him in six hours' time. Remove the doe and carry her quietly back to her own hutch and leave her with a titbit, perhaps an extra bit of hay or a little freshly picked grass.

In any cases when there is any doubt about a successful mating having taken place, return the doe to the buck in about six hours' time. She will probably mate successfully then. Always record the mating on both buck's and doe's cards and make an entry in the rabbitry calendar to put in a nestbox or nesting materials on the twenty-fifth day and enter the expected date of kindling, on the thirty-first day.

The doe has pushed the hay to the
sides and covered the babies with
plenty of her own belly fur. The
partial lid is optional

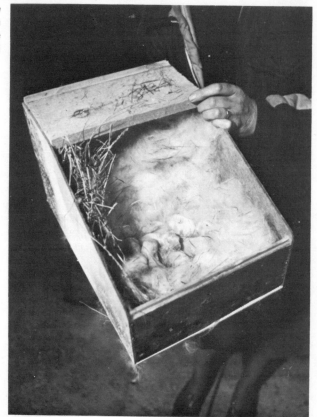

A very moden breeding pen of
galvanised wire mesh with top
opening and a sunken nesting area,
which is proving satisfactory in
commercial use. Note the record cards
on the feed hoppers. The doe in the
right-hand pen has a pronounced
dewlap, which is quite normal in large
breeds. It is a pad of fatty tissue

Remating Cycles

This is very important for the provision of a steady flow of meat rabbits. Once a doe has begun to breed she must be kept steadily at work or she will run to fat and become unable to breed. So when her babies are three to four weeks of age she can be mated again and the babies weaned into another pen or hutch. The doe's milk supply is beginning to shrink at about that time and she is in good condition for the next litter. Some commercial rabbit producers remate almost immediately after the litter is born but I do not recommend this for the home rabbit breeder. There are too many problems of feeding, stress for the doe and a shorter working life for her. I do not like the idea of making does feed one litter while carrying another. Equally it is not good practice to leave the young too long with the doe. If they are left for six weeks or so, there can be overcrowding in the hutch and the doe will certainly be overfeeding herself from the feed pots. These have to be kept sufficiently full for there to be a little left by the next feed, for the babies' sakes. The doe will have had far too big a share if they are together after about the fourth week. Too much food for the doe, too much risk of no further breeding!

Care of the Stud Buck

The stud buck is a very important rabbit as his influence is felt right through the rabbitry. He can manage from ten to fifteen does in a big unit, so that he needs extra care in a small one to keep him fit but not fat. He must be of good type and come from fast growing and healthy stock. The buck must have his own hutch or pen from the age of ten weeks if he is to develop properly and escape fights with others. Like all rabbits he needs plenty of fresh air without draughts, and good food in moderate amounts. Handle him often to accustom him to human hands and to give him confidence in his handler. If the rabbit house has electric light, avoid placing his pen directly under a light bulb. Too bright a light can retard his breeding powers—in contrast to the doe who needs light to stimulate hers.

Care of the Doe

Does should be separated soon after they reach twelve weeks of age into their own breeding pens or hutches. They too need good food and plenty of fresh air. Get the doe accustomed to handling so that the necessary inspections and management can be carried out. A well-handled doe can make all the difference to successful matings. Just before she is due to kindle in a wire-mesh pen, give her a nestbox with plenty of soft hay and keep a clean, dry, empty feedbag on top of the pen above the nestbox. This stops down-draughts and keeps the litter cosy and quiet. Does in solid-floor hutches also need plenty of good soft hay in the nesting area, which should be shuttered in front and about three parts up the wire door. About twenty-four hours before she kindles she will lose her appetite, but this is quite natural and about twenty-four hours afterwards she will be eating normally again. Keep a good supply of fresh clean drinking water always available. A little freshly picked grass or part of a cabbage leaf or other juicy green food will tempt her appetite

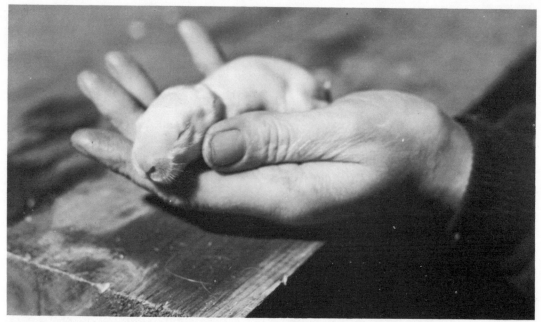

One of the babies from the nest, five days old and showing the flat ears and closed eyes

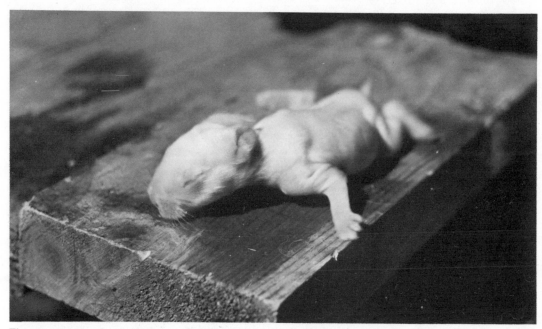

The same baby sprawled out to show the fur growth at that age and the plump belly of a well-fed baby. While being photographed it was trying to wriggle back to the warmth of the nestbox!

Siesta time. A three week old litter of New Zealand Whites with another penful of litter and doe behind them

The same litter showing the typical conformation of good young meat rabbits. There are nine in the litter, two having hidden behind the doe

and start the milk flow. A doe with a large litter will need extra water, and may need two containers. She will need about 0.5–0.6 litres (1–1¼ pt.) of water when she has a litter of eight at three weeks old.

Care of the Litter

A good doe will regulate the amount of hay and fur covering her babies according to the temperature. If she eats a lot of the hay in the nest she is not getting enough fibre in her diet. Give her extra hay each day, otherwise the nest will be scanty and cold for the babies. If the litter is getting plenty of doe's milk they will not come out of the nest until the eighteenth day, but their eyes will be open by the tenth day. They are born naked with eyes shut and in a very few days the fur grows. Even before their eyes open they will begin to nibble the softer stalks of hay in the nest. This is Nature's way of teaching them to take solid food and starting the weaning process.

Always inspect the nest when the doe has settled down after the births to remove any weaklings, mis-shaped or injured babies. Any thin babies with flat tummies should be removed, for they will never do any good. A brief daily look at the nest enables the breeder to see that all the babies are feeding well; in a big litter there may be one or two who do not get to a teat.

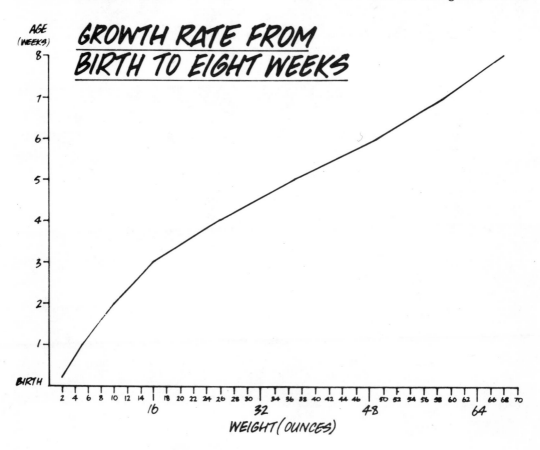

GROWTH RATE FROM BIRTH TO EIGHT WEEKS

AGE (WEEKS)

WEIGHT (OUNCES)

Weaning and Rearing

A young rabbit is ready for weaning when it is running about the pen or hutch freely and can feed itself and drink from the water container. In fast-growing meat rabbits this occurs at about 3–4 weeks. Each baby should weigh about 700 g (1½ lb.) at three weeks and put on another 450 g (1 lb.) each week until it is about ten weeks old. After that age the rate of growth in normal circumstances slows down, while the feed intake rises. Place the young rabbits in another pen and remate the doe. The doe is calmer and happier if left in her own pen and the babies moved. If green foods are fed to all the rabbits it is wise to omit them from the diet of newly weaned youngsters for a few days, slowly reintroducing them over a further few days. Young rabbits are very greedy and without the balancing action of the doe's milk tend to eat too much green food and pellets. A little extra hay will help balance the diet. The meat rabbits should be ready for killing at nine to ten weeks but if some are required as replacement stock or for expansion these should be selected and moved to single pens. Keep careful records of each rabbit intended for breeding. Rabbits on pellets and hay should have the amount of pellets reduced to keep them in hard condition, not fat. Up to ten weeks of age feed them as much as they clear before the next due feed, but after that age limit the pellets to about 112 g (4 oz.). A little more may be needed for very large strains of rabbit or very healthy, energetic stock.

Selection of Breeding Stock

The requirements for good breeding stock have been considered in the Section 'Buying your Stock'. How to choose them from one's own herd is a little different because one is on one's own! It is one of the joys of home rabbit breeding with pure-bred stock that one can rear one's own replacement stock and do much to improve the herd's performance, whether small or large. There are two important rules to be observed.

1. Choose future breeding stock from the best litters. There should be at least seven reared and fast growing, and the parents and litter must be healthy at all times. Any rabbit that has had a setback or whose litter-mates have had one should never be used for breeding. This would lower the standard of the herd quicker than almost any other cause.
2. Careful records must be kept to ensure that brother and sister are never mated together, even if of different litters from the same parents. In a small herd a new buck must be introduced after three generations have been bred from the original one. His daughters and grand-daughters may be mated back to him but unless the breeder is experienced it is safer to introduce new blood regularly.

False Pregnancies

This is a condition in which a doe, usually a maiden doe, thinks she is pregnant and all her hormones work as if she is. Then at the eighteenth day she reverts to normal. It is caused sometimes by leaving young does

Week old baby rabbit, with the fur growing. The ears are deaf and are held flat on the back for the first eight days; the eyes are closed until the tenth day

Rabbit of two weeks old, well formed, ears mobile, with clear bright eye and alert position

Three weeks old and putting on weight nicely. Well furred and alert in appearance

Healthy rabbit, showing the straight back and wide loins and shoulders of a good meat rabbit

together in one pen too long, or by the near proximity of a buck. If a mated doe does not have a litter when due or when she makes a nest and plucks fur about the tenth to seventeenth day after mating she may have been having a false pregnancy. If she has not put on weight by the nineteenth day it is useful to remate her on that date. If she is really pregnant it will not matter, and if not, time will have been saved.

Keeping up Production

In order to keep up the flow of meat rabbits the young does must be mated when they are ready and then remated regularly for the whole of their working lives. A doe will occasionally miss her mating and then start production again quite happily at the next mating. This is Nature's way of giving her a rest sometimes, but if a doe fails to have a litter after several matings check to see that she and the buck are in good health and that there is no error in management to cause this. If all appears well and there is still no litter, cull the doe after a month or so of repeated attempts to get her in kindle. She may be barren, too fat or just lazy. Check the buck to be sure he has litters by other does and that it is not his fault. If the doe has fed a large litter well she may be a bit thin, but will pick up condition quite quickly when they are weaned, and be ready for her next litter.

Bucks give useful service for three years or more but the does need replacing after two years. One sign is the size of the litters and the number of litters reared. Older rabbits make excellent stews, etc., so they are not wasted even if no longer of use for breeding!

Fostering Baby Rabbits

Fostering baby rabbits is possible but not to be recommended, as there is a risk of passing disease from one doe to another. If it is necessary to foster, it must be done before the rabbits are more than four days old. The doe is removed from her pen and the babies put into her nest and covered with the nesting material. The doe is then put back and given a titbit. There is no need for the old-fashioned rubbing hands in messes, etc.; if the doe is accustomed to being handled she will not resent the operation. Only babies from healthy litters and where the doe is fit but cannot feed so many should be fostered. The receiving doe must be healthy too.

Cannibalism in Does

Occasionally a doe will eat some or all of her babies, usually at birth or within a few days. This may be due to a lack of drinking water for her, or to a deficiency in her diet. Sometimes it is due to a little too much eagerness on her part to clean up the afterbirths. If a baby has been injured at birth she may eat it in an effort to clean up. If a doe repeats this with the next litter, cull her. It will never be curable.

The Structure of the Rabbit

The Skeleton

The rabbit has been called the poor man's cattle, for it can provide food and clothing and be kept economically in a comparatively small space. It is a small fur-bearing mammal, herbivorous, and does not require meat products in its food. The main features of the skeleton are the short neck, fairly long backbone with much of the meat found on the hindquarters, both loins and back legs. The bones may be large and heavy for its size, but in the best meat breeds they are comparatively light and fine.

The rabbit has two types of movement. Before weaning it uses the back feet independently of each other. Thereafter it uses them together in a hopping movement. This movement throws up the tail exposing the white scut under it, a sign of warning in the wild. They also have a sound warning; the thump of the back feet. Both bucks and does thump, but restless bucks with not enough work to do are apt to thump around their hutch so much that they make their hocks sore. The muscular development for hopping results in greater strength in the hindquarters, hence the extra meat! Meaty forequarters have to be bred into a strain.

Rabbits, like other animals, sleep lightly most of the time, but I have surprised rabbits fast asleep which are quite alarmed when wakened. When they are really fast asleep they lie on one side in a relaxed position. At other times they crouch rather than lie, with their ears at rest. Young rabbits in the nest can, when frightened, leap to extraordinary heights, even right out of the nestbox.

Fur and Wool

Only one breed, the Angora, carries wool, and as it is not a meat breed it is not relevant here. Rabbit fur varies from the longer normal type of fur which may be up to 30 mm ($1\frac{1}{4}$ in.) in length, to the short Rex fur, at 12 mm ($\frac{1}{2}$ in.). This is a lovely plush coat found in many colours, but the breeds carrying it are slow to mature for meat. The other type is the Satin, with a lovely sheen which is found right down the shaft of each hair, and not only on the top of the coat as in other types. Fur may be harsh or soft, thin or dense with a wide variety of colours, white and black and nearly every shade between. Some rabbits have colour patterns and markings, shadings and different layers of colour in each hair as in the Chinchillas. In all but one of the normal fur breeds the coat should have resistance, i.e. spring back into place when rubbed the wrong way, from tail to head. The fur of the Siberian can be rubbed either way without causing it to spring. The Rex fur is short and dense and does not lie in any obvious direction. It has none of the longer guard hairs found in other fur and even the whiskers are scanty and not very long.

The condition of the coat is a good indication of the rabbit's health. If it is glossy and sleek, lying properly against the skin, it shows a healthy rabbit. A sick rabbit has a dry, brittle, dull coat with the hairs standing up like spikes, a staring coat. The density and texture of the coat may be influenced by a number of factors, including heredity, feeding and environment. Rabbits kept out of doors tend to have denser coats than those in houses, when other factors are equal.

The Breathing System

The rabbit breathes through its nose and has a complicated system for warming the air before it reaches the lungs. It needs plenty of fresh air, without direct draughts and is harmed by dust and fumes. The first thing one notices about the rabbit's nose is its nostrils with their continual twitching. This is a rhythmic movement but is not necessarily at the same rate as the breathing. The rabbit's sense of smell is very keen, and it reacts swiftly to irritation such as dust and fumes by sneezing. The rabbit in health does not show any discharge from the nose. If there is a discharge as in colds or other illness the rabbit will try to clear the trouble with its front paws. As a result the inner sides of legs and paws show dampness, and possibly messy discharge. The rabbit's lungs and their efficient working are the keynotes to successful rabbit breeding, hence the emphasis on good ventilation.

Like all young things baby rabbits breathe faster than adults, in fact nearly double the adult rate of forty-five per minute. Under extreme stress, pneumonia or heat prostration this rate may be so fast as to be almost uncountable.

The Digestive System

There are two rather unusual features in the rabbit's digestive system:
1. It depends largely on bulk to push the food in the stomach through the valve to the small intestine. This results in a definite need for fibre in the diet and a certain amount of bulk intake.
2. It passes a special type of pellet at night which it takes into its mouth directly from the anus. This supplements part of the feed intake and aids digestion and nutrition. This special pellet and its circulation is known as coprophagy and the pellets as soft pellets.

The normal faecal dropping is a harder, larger pellet, and is passed both by day and night. A rabbit cannot vomit so that it is impossible to make it vomit poison if swallowed. This means that poisoning is almost always fatal. The digestive process starts in the rabbit's mouth which has the cleft in the top lip continued to the base of the nostrils so that it can use the chisel teeth on grass and hay. A rabbit's upper jaw should close exactly on the lower so that the chisel or incisor teeth can be kept ground down to the correct level. If there is any misfit the teeth continue to grow and result in the condition known as buck teeth or malocclusion.

After passing down the gullet the food enters the stomach where further digestion takes place. When sufficient food is ready its pressure opens the valve and it passes into the small intestine. Regular feeding is important for the rabbit to keep a steady flow for this bulk movement.

Fibrous foods such as hay supply this bulk when the ration of pellets is finished, and avoids alternate emptying and gorging.

The intestines complete the process of digestion and act as organs of absorption for the nutriment of the diet. Between the small and large intestines we find the caecum, a curious organ which holds semi-liquid material and ends in the appendix. The large intestine then passes the mass onwards and faecal pellets begin to form. There may be as many as a hundred in the gut, soft at first but hardening as the water and nutriments are absorbed by the walls of the large intestine.

The liver, gall bladder, spleen and pancreas also play their parts in providing juices to aid digestion.

The Liver

This is the largest of the digestive organs, and is found in the abdominal cavity. It has two lobes, is smooth and soft in a healthy rabbit.

The Gall Bladder

This is found under the liver among its folds and contains bile. The gall bladder is greenish in colour, and as the bile is very acid it must not be allowed to splash on to the meat when a carcase is being dressed.

The spleen and pancreas are important but need not trouble the home rabbit keeper.

Rabbit Droppings

Faecal pellets vary with the type of food, its quantity and contents. An adult of 2.5–3 kg ($5\frac{1}{2}$–$6\frac{1}{2}$ lb.) will pass about 150 pellets per day. The normal pellet also varies in colour according to the feed given, from a light straw colour to a darkish brown. The rabbit keeper soon gets to know what is normal for his rabbits and is quick to spot any difference and to know the cause.

The soft pellet of coprophagy is secreted in the stomach and is soft and brown. They are seldom seen as the rabbit takes them direct from the anus. All rabbits which have been weaned perform the phenomenon but have not been seen to do so while still receiving doe's milk.

Sexing Young Rabbits

The buck's external sexual organ shows as a rounded point. In the adult male it is easily seen flanked on either side by the sacs containing the testes. The young rabbit should be held in the left hand, belly upwards, and tail towards the fingers. Using finger and thumb of the other hand press gently on either side of the vent region when the male organ will show as a small circle. Always handle the rabbit very gently while sexing as it is very easy to damage the delicate organs. The doe's external organ shows as a slit much closer to the vent, and may be seen by handling the doe in the same way as the buck.

Reproductive Organs—the Doe

The doe has a uterus which has two horns and two Fallopian tubes for the reception of the ova or eggs. These come from the two ovaries, which are small organs situated behind the kidneys. The external opening from the uterus is known as the vagina and the folds of flesh around it are the vulva. The ripe ova are passed from the ovaries via the Fallopian tubes to the

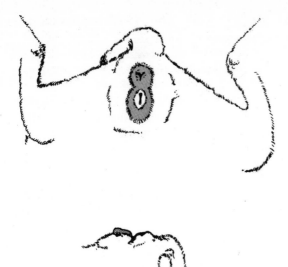

Top view, baby doe rabbit, showing female organ as a slit. Lower view shows the flat appearance of the organ

The doe also has milk-secreting glands known as the mammary glands, the teats of which are exposed when the doe plucks her belly fur for lining the nest. The teats are situated on either side of the belly, and there may be six to ten of them. A good doe of New Zealand White or Californian breed should have eight good teats to enable her to feed a big litter. The most active ones are usually those between her back legs, diminishing as they are located towards her chest. The hormones controlling the secretion of the milk begin to be active during the later stages of pregnancy, so that the doe has the first milk or colostrum ready for the babies within twenty-four hours of birth. The suckling of the babies stimulates the flow of milk still more. The period of lactation lasts from birth to a peak at about fourteen to fifteen days, then decreases until the fifth week or weaning, whichever comes first. At the peak a good doe will produce about 140 g (5 oz.) per day. The milk is very rich, and its proportions are such that it almost impossible to find a substitute feed for baby rabbits. This is why it seldom pays to try to feed orphan babies artificially. Doe's milk has extra solids, proteins and fats, but less milk sugar than cow's milk.

uterus where they are fertilised and develop into full-term baby rabbits. If the doe is too fat there will be layers of fat around the open ends of the Fallopian tubes so that the tiny eggs will be unable to enter and will be lost in the abdominal cavity. This is one reason why does cannot breed, and even if slimmed down the fat around internal organs does not completely disappear. This can result in permanent sterility for the doe.

A doe rabbit does not have any well-defined period of heat like other female animals, so she can be mated success-fully at many times. She will mate satisfactorily when showing signs of readiness, when her vulva will be swollen and reddish, with some moisture. She will also mate perfectly well at times when she shows no sign.

Reproductive Organs—the Buck

The buck has the external organ, the penis, which also contains the channel for the passing of urine from the kidneys. It is the tip of the penis which is the circular point to be looked for in sexing baby rabbits. The mature buck has a pair of testicles each in a sac on either side of the penis. If the testicles are not visible he will not be fertile.

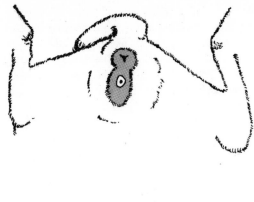

Top view, baby buck, with rounded male organ; the lower view shows the raised pointed protrusion of the organ when examined

Always inspect the buck before offering him a doe to ensure that he is clean and dry underneath the tail. There should be no sign of inflammation around the vent area.

The Circulation of the Blood

The heart is the powerful pump which propels the blood around the body, at one stage sending it through the lungs for purification. The home rabbit is not likely to suffer any abnormality of this system so that details are unnecessary.

The Kidneys and Adrenal Glands

The two kidneys are situated at the back of the abdomen on either side of the spinal column. These are glands of excretion for getting rid of some of the waste materials from the digestive system. The urinary bladder excretes the urine, which can vary in colour quite considerably. It can be cloudy or clear in a healthy rabbit. The amount is slightly larger in bucks but it is also affected by the water intake. The urine can be tinged red if too much dandelion is given. The adrenals are small glands just above the kidneys.

The Pituitary Gland

This is situated in the skull and has a wide-ranging effect on the body's workings. Light stimulates it and it secretes several hormones influencing the reproductive system. It is also concerned with the secretion of insulin in the pancreas and with the correct functioning of other glands.

The Eyes

Rabbits' eyes are rather prominent and have a third eyelid, the nictitating membrane, which it uses for protection of the eye. It will be noticed that the third eyelid is used instead of blinking when there is irritation of the eye. The newborn rabbit is blind, opening its eyes at about the tenth day. The colour of the eyes is different in different breeds. The Albino breeds have pink eyes, due to the absence of any colour cells.

The Ears

The rabbit's ears are very sensitive to sound and play some part in the regulation of body temperature. The large outer lobes are very mobile to allow for the collection of sound waves from a wide area around the rabbit. With the exception of the Lop and Half Lop breeds it carries its ears erect in health and lays them back along the skull when resting. Drooping ears can be a sign of ill-health. Red and congested ears show that the rabbit has a high temperature or is suffering from heat stress. The internal ear is very complicated and deep. In severe cold, such as in Alaska, it has been known for the external ears to become frost-bitten and fall off. The rabbits have survived and bred well but looked most odd. The baby rabbit is deaf for the first eight days of its life.

Rabbit Diseases

Rabbits are really very healthy, hardy little animals provided that they are fed and housed properly. The home-bred rabbit can suffer from a few troubles that are curable and one or two for which there is no satisfactory remedy at present known. Usually if illness occurs in the rabbit it is due to some error in management, such as poor ventilation or faulty feeding. Prevention is better than trying to cure, an old saying especially true when applied to rabbit keeping. Prevention really means keeping the rules of good rabbitry management and keeping a very keen eye on every rabbit every day. In this way any faults can be corrected before any great harm is done, and if illness does come in spite of every care then it can be dealt with promptly.

The Rules of Good Management

1. Start with good healthy stock from a reliable source.

2. Provide good housing and pens or hutches with no draughts.

3. Allow for plenty of fresh air.

4. Give good, suitable food and clean water.

5. Ensure absolute cleanliness in the rabbitry.

6. Keep records so that any trouble can be quickly traced to its source.

Veterinary Services

These can be expensive, and many troubles can be traced back to management, so that it might be a waste of the veterinary surgeon's time to call him in. However, in cases of severe outbreaks of disease or when the rabbit keeper cannot clear up the trouble, call for veterinary aid. It is seldom worthwhile to try to cure sick rabbits but preventative medicines can be helpful. A sick rabbit suffers such a setback in condition that it will never make a good healthy rabbit even when it seems better. Cull it, and save wasting food and space on it.

Chills

This is a common killer of baby rabbits, even in the nest, and is caused by a direct draught on them, either from above or from a crack in the floor of the nest box or area. In cold weather see that there is a good wooden floor in the nest, or place a sheet of marine plywood between the nest box and the pen floor. Plenty of soft meadow hay is the best nesting material, but the doe will dig right to the floor to deposit her babies. This is why a warm floor is essential. Chill usually affects baby rabbits during the first fortnight of their lives, sudden death being the first and only obvious symptom. Often the whole litter dies overnight. Preventing the illness by keeping litters warm and the rabbit house of equable temperature is the only possible treatment.

Colds

A rabbit with a cold has a running nose and sneezes, and a sneezing rabbit is dangerous until the cause has been found. It will also sneeze because of dust, ammonia fumes or a foreign body in its nose, but when these causes are removed it will stop.

If the running eyes and nose are due to an infection then there is a real problem. The sick rabbit must be isolated from all the others, preferably under a veranda or other shelter out of doors. If the cold does not clear up within a week or so, then it is better to kill the victim and burn or bury the carcase, for it probably has an infection which can be passed very easily to the other rabbits. Colds must be prevented by quick isolation of any suspect cases and by never buying stock from a 'sneezing' herd. Never introduce a newly-purchased rabbit into the main rabbitry until it has spent twenty-one days in quarantine, i.e. in a pen right away from the main house or rows of hutches. If a rabbit has not developed any symptoms of illness in that time it is considered safe to join the other rabbits.

Pneumonia

This sometimes appears in a rabbit herd housed indoors and is almost always due to faulty ventilation, chill in young rabbits or as a secondary complication in rabbits of poor general stamina. The victim is miserable, huddled in a corner of its pen with a rate of breathing almost too quick to count. It dies within twenty-four hours. Attention to the quality of the diet and to the general conditions in which the rabbits are living will help to prevent further cases.

It is noticeable that rabbits housed in warm, weatherproof hutches out of doors seldom get colds or pneumonia. The danger lies in stuffy indoor conditions and in too wide a range of temperature from day to night.

Coccidiosis

This is one of the most common ailments found in home-bred rabbits and is not so easy to clear from the herd. Every rabbit carries at least a few coccidia (the organism responsible for the complaint) just as most humans carry the germ responsible for pneumonia which can flare up into an acute attack when the conditions are right for it. In coccidiosis this flare-up takes place when the rabbit is a little less than fit, due perhaps to wrong feeding, under-feeding or when it has suffered from extra stress.

There are two kinds of coccidiosis, one of which affects the rabbit's **liver**. This is not usually fatal and the rabbit appears to show no signs until the liver is examined after slaughter and reveals small white spots. They are pin-headed and the more and larger the spots the worse the trouble. These livers must not be eaten although the rest of the rabbit is perfectly safe for human consumption. However, the condition must be dealt with in the rest of the stock or production will suffer and none of the delicious rabbit livers be eatable. The life cycle of the coccidia is like a chain which must be broken to stop further cases. The rabbit passes the eggs with its droppings; these lie around, and will thrive if allowed warm, damp conditions. Dirty floors and warm, damp heaps of droppings in corners or on the solid floors are ideal! The rabbit then gets some of these eggs into its mouth, by eating dirty food or licking itself underneath, and the cycle starts again. The means of prevention are strict hygiene and a check on the does to see which of them are having litters with these bad livers. Cull does that do not respond to treatment. This is one of the diseases that does pay for treatment, and for the use of preventative drugs known as coccidiostats. These may be added to the pellets by the miller or given under veterinary supervision in the drinking water as a prevention. To treat suspected cases the drug may be given in stronger doses in the drinking water. If pellets with an added coccidiostat are used, only small amounts of hay should be added to the diet, or the small doses in the feed will be reduced below an effective level. If a mixed diet is being fed, the drug should be given in the drinking water.

The other form of coccidiosis attacks the **intestines** and is much more likely to kill its victim. The rabbit looks thin, has a staring coat, a razor back and, in the early stages, an unusually large appetite. All the extra food does not result in even a normal growth rate. The irritation caused in the intestines prevents the rabbit from absorbing the nourishment it should via the cells of the intestines. It is useless to try to cure a bad case, but the rest of the litter must be treated as a prevention against further cases. Water-soluble drugs are usually given to the newly-weaned rabbits for five days, or for three days, followed by two rest days and then three more days. Young breeding stock should be similarly treated again just before coming into the breeding pen. The sick rabbit should be taken from the pen or hutch and if it is kept on solid floor the bedding should be cleaned out and freshly given. This may help stop any further rabbits becoming infected. Strict attention to hygiene and to keeping the rabbits comfortable and well fed are the best preventative measures.

Enteritis or Scours

The word enteritis covers a number of conditions affecting the digestive system of the rabbit, most of which follow a set pattern of stomach upset and inflammation of some part of the intestines leading to scours and death. In serious cases an infection by some germ or germs accompanies the upset but it is seldom that the infection arrives first. Causes include a diet in which the ingredients are not properly balanced, the rabbit having been fed too much protein; too little fibre (hay); wet or frozen greens or roots; mouldy greens, roots or hay; pellets contaminated by rats or mice; or dirty feeding utensils. Occasionally cases of enteritis will occur in the rabbitry run on the best lines, where the strictest rules of health and hygiene are observed. In these cases send for veterinary aid to combat the infection.

Young newly-weaned rabbits are often the victims of scours. This may be due to a move to a colder pen or house, or to allowing them too much green food and not enough hay, or too many pellets. It pays to reduce the rations for healthy weaners for the first few days—they are noted for their greed! The first sign of scours may be a rabbit looking thoroughly miserable, perhaps huddled over or near its drinker. The vent area will become fouled with the semi-liquid droppings and the rabbit will not eat. There is no cure. The rabbit must be removed and killed, and the carcase burnt. Pens and hutches must be thoroughly cleaned and disinfected after cases of illness.

Mastitis

Mastitis or inflammation of the milk glands in a nursing doe will sometimes occur if her litter does not take all the milk. It is also caused by injury, a rough floor or edge to the nest box, or a scratch from a baby's claw. During the early days after she has kindled, put a hand gently under her belly and the glands will be soft if normal, but if a bit hard and hotter than they should be she may wince with pain when touched. In the home rabbitry it pays to lift her on to a table and apply warm cloths to the parts. After a couple of applications it should be possible to express very gently a few drops of milk from the affected teats, and then the babies will do the rest. If the condition does not respond after two or three applications of heat call the veterinary surgeon as the doe may have an infection which needs treatment with an antibiotic drug. This is one of the occasions when the expense of veterinary aid is justified, but if the doe gets mastitis again she had better be culled.

Ear Canker

Rabbits can get a mite in the ears which causes the ear to be filled with a crusty discharge and its channels to become very inflamed. It is quite simple to cure the condition but takes a little time and patience. Clean out the crusty discharge with damp cotton wool on an orange stick. Apply one of the preparations sold by chemists for ear canker, possibly a benzyl benzoate one. Repeat every five days until the ear is quite normal again. Two or three applications will be necessary to ensure that both mites and eggs are destroyed completely. As the infection is easily passed from one rabbit to another wash the hands after dealing with a rabbit with it, and thoroughly disinfect the pen or hutch when it is cured.

Sore Hocks

The hock or 'elbow' on the back leg is apt to get sore, and possibly rubbed bare of fur followed by soreness of the skin beneath. This may be due to a number of causes including the rabbit doing more than usual stamping on his floor, a sagging wire floor or rough solid floor, or because the fur is thin and poor on its feet. The hock may be red and sore, have broken skin or scabs from infected sores. There is not a lot that can be done except remove any obvious causes in the pen, and put the rabbit on to soft dry bedding such as soft wood shavings. The sores may be cleaned with warm soapy water and treated with an ointment such as iodine or a zinc preparation. If the coat is poor, check that the rabbits are not undernourished and see that a harsher strain of buck is introduced to improve the coats. Very soft-coated rabbits such as Rex are not usually kept on wire floors. If the condition is very bad before it is noticed it may be better to cull the rabbit, for it will get progressively worse. Sore hocks can be prevented and, if present in early stages, cleared from the herd. Check all equipment for snags and rough places, especially floors. Wire floors must be strong enough to remain flat and not sag. Gauge 12 or 14 is best, with the rabbit is unable to eat and would die of starvation if not seen in time. It must be killed, and if of market weight is quite edible. The tendency can be bred out of a herd, and no further breeding must take place between the parents of the sufferer. His litter brothers and sisters should not be used for breeding as they may carry the tendency. With careful records and strict culling the tendency will disappear.

No one will own this buck! He has a typical condition of sore hocks, due to general ill-health rather than to poor fur on the feet. In fact he has well-furred feet

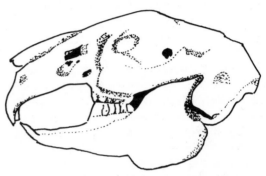

Normal formation of rabbit's jaws showing the incisors meeting properly to ensure that they are kept ground to the correct size

shorter cross wires lying underneath the floor. If it is the fur at fault, keep careful records of sufferers and their parents and gradually get them out of the herd, bringing in breeding stock with the firmer coats bred in by a new harsher coated buck. Occasionally the condition may be caused by a rabbit's having his claws too long. Keep them clipped properly. If the claws are too long the rabbit walks badly, leaning back on the hock. This can occur in the front feet too.

Buck Teeth

This is a nasty condition in which the rabbit's teeth are not aligned correctly when it bites, so that consequently they are not kept worn to size. The teeth grow too long and in the end the

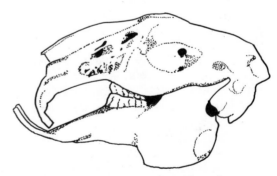

The grossly distorted jaw formation of malocclusion, or buck teeth. Due to an inherited condition the teeth do not meet and thus grow out of the correct line with disastrous results. The rabbit cannot eat

Worms

Rabbits do not suffer much from worms with the exception of a harmless small white worm. Treatment is not often necessary. However, they can become infected by a tape worm, via the droppings of cats and dogs. The eggs of the tape worm are found on green food fouled by dogs and cats. In the rabbit the form may be of a cyst in the skin or white spots around the internal organs. In any case kill and burn the rabbit and on no account feed it to a pet or the eggs will be passed on.

Injuries

In well-managed rabbitries there are few injuries, apart from an occasional bite from a pen-mate, scratches from wire snags or more vicious bites from a fight when bucks are together in one pen too long. Separate bucks kept for breeding when they are not more than twelve weeks old. Clean wounds with TCP or other mild disinfectant, cutting away matted and soiled fur. A bad tear may need stitches. Prevent fighting and watch pens and houses for snags.

Myxomatosis

This is primarily a disease of wild rabbits and is very seldom found among home-bred rabbits. Rabbits kept in sheds or houses which can be protected from biting insects (mosquitoes and fleas) are less vulnerable than those in outside hutches. Keep the land around the rabbitry free from wild rabbits, vermin and rubbish. Keep cats and dogs out of the rabbit house. If these rules are kept there should be no cause for alarm. However, there is a preventative vaccine which gives rabbits immunity for about eight to nine months. It should be used if the disease is very bad in the area among any wild rabbits. If the rabbit has already caught the disease the vaccine will lessen the severity and it will probably recover. The symptoms of myxomatosis are well known: Sores around eyes, mouth and head, and the pitiful starved look. If it has been necessary to vaccinate the home rabbits, give breeding stock a booster dose after nine months. The veterinary surgeon will do this for you if you are not used to treating animals.

Fur Chewing

This is not strictly a disease but does occur sometimes. The rabbits chew their own or other rabbits' fur. This may be due to an error in the balance of feeds in the diet or to a shortage of crude fibre, such as when hay is not fed. It may also be due to boredom or overcrowding. Feed hay, or add a little extra to that already given, and the trouble will clear up and the fur grow again.

Recipes

There are over a hundred recipes for using our delicious rabbit meat but here are a few to whet your appetite, and to show how versatile it can be.

Rabbit Broth

1 old rabbit
28 g (1 oz.) flour
2 onions
Seasoning
56 g (2 oz.) butter or margarine
1 litre (1¾ pt.) water

METHOD

Melt the butter in a pan, and fry the rabbit joints until brown. Add the onions and water, season well and simmer for two hours. Mix the flour with a little cold water, stir into the soup and simmer for another five minutes. Strain and serve with some of the meat which has been diced into small cubes.

Roast Rabbit

1 or 2 rabbits
770 g (1¾ lb.) potatoes
450 g (1 lb.) sausages
Dripping or bacon fat
Rashers of bacon to cover the rabbits
112 g (4 oz.) breadcrumbs
56 g (2 oz.) chopped suet
1 tablespoon chopped parsley
Pinch of thyme leaves
1 egg
Salt and pepper

METHOD

Prepare the stuffing by mixing the crumbs, suet, herbs and seasoning. Beat the egg and add to the mixture to bind it. Pack into the rabbit carcase with the heart and kidneys. Sew up the belly with fine twine or skewer it, bend the front legs between the back ones and lay on its side. Cover with the bacon rashers, place in roasting tin and surround with the potatoes. Add the dripping or bacon fat and a little water to cover the base of the pan. Roast in a fairly hot oven for half an hour, then in a moderate heat for another hour. Prick and add sausages to the pan and finish with the lid off. Serve with gravy made from the pan drippings, seasoning and a little gravy browning. Serve also with bread sauce.

Cold Rabbit with Salad

Serve the rabbit nicely jointed on a bed of lettuce or endive, with as big a variety of colourful vegetables as are seasonable. Tomato, radish, beet, peas, french beans, chives, cucumber, the variety is endless. Serve with mayonnaise or a home-made salad dressing.

Marrow with Rabbit Stuffing

1 marrow
Cold rabbit meat, minced or chopped
    finely
Any stuffing also left over
Cooked sausages and bacon
A little chopped raw onion
Seasoning and a little good gravy
Dripping

METHOD

Cut the marrow in half lengthways, peel it and remove the pith and seeds. Mix the meat, onion, seasoning, etc., with the gravy to make a moist filling. Put into the hollowed marrow, tie the halves together with tape. Place in an ovenproof dish with a good lump of dripping, cover with greased paper. Bake for $1\frac{1}{2}$ hours in a good oven, basting occasionally and serve with a good brown gravy.

Hot Pot with Forcemeat Balls

1 rabbit
About $\frac{1}{2}$ cup of each of as many
    vegetables as are in season (carrots,
    swede, celery, onion, kohl rabi,
    beans, etc.)
Seasoning
28 g (1 oz.) flour
Gravy browning
Potatoes
Forcemeat balls
112 g (4 oz.) breadcrumbs
56 g (2 oz.) chopped suet
1 tablespoon parsley, finely chopped
1 teaspoon grated lemon rind
Pinch thyme, salt, pepper
1 egg

METHOD

Mix the dry ingredients and bind with beaten egg, form into balls. Place the rabbit joints in a large casserole, with the vegetables and the balls. Mix the seasoning, flour and gravy browning with a little water and pour over the meat. Slice the potatoes and lay on top, add more water or stock to half fill the dish. Cover with a greased paper and the lid. Cook in a slow oven for 3 hours.

Rabbit à la King

This is an American recipe and can be used with success for an old rabbit.

1 rabbit or 3 cups of diced, cooked
    rabbit meat
2 cups cream
4 tablespoons butter
2 tablespoons flour
1 green pepper, chopped
450 g (1 lb.) mushrooms, cut in pieces
2 egg yolks
1 teaspoon minced onion
1 tablespoon lemon juice
Salt, paprika
$\frac{1}{2}$ cup chopped pimentoes

METHOD

Wipe the dressed rabbit with a damp cloth, place on a rack in a kettle, add $\frac{1}{2}$ teaspoon salt, barely cover with water, partly cover the kettle and simmer for $1\frac{1}{2}$ hours, or until the meat is tender. Let it cool in the broth, drain, remove the meat from the bones and cut into even-sized pieces. Heat the cream in a double boiler. Blend the flour with 2 tablespoons of the butter and stir into the cream until thickened. Melt the remaining butter in a pan, add the green pepper and mushrooms, and cook for a few moments over low heat. Beat the egg yolks, stir a small quantity of the thickened cream into them and add to the rest of the sauce. Stir in the mushrooms, pepper, lemon juice, paprika, and salt to taste. Add the diced rabbit and pimento. When the mixture is heated thoroughly serve in pastry shells or on crisp toast.

Rabbit Liver Pâté

Rabbit livers make a very savoury pâté for use as sandwich filling, to spread on biscuits or toast, to serve with salad. Simmer the livers in a little boiling water for 10 minutes, then drain. Mash the livers with a fork, remove any stringy tissues, and blend with finely chopped olives, minced onion, mayonnaise and dashes of tabasco sauce and paprika. Chill before using.

Rabbit Supreme

1 rabbit, (1–1$\frac{1}{2}$ kg [2$\frac{1}{4}$–3$\frac{1}{4}$ lb.])
1 cup milk
2 cups cream of mushroom soup
1 bay leaf
Salt and pepper, and dash of curry powder if liked

METHOD

Roll serving sized pieces of rabbit in flour, seasoned with salt and pepper, lay in buttered casserole. Add the other ingredients, cover and bake in slow oven (325 degrees) for 1$\frac{1}{2}$ hours. Add more milk or water if the liquid evaporates too much. Cook for the last 15 minutes with the cover off to brown the rabbit lightly. Serve sprinkled with parsley.

Rabbit Soufflé

56 g (2 oz.) finely chopped rabbit
28 g (1 oz.) butter
14 g ($\frac{1}{2}$ oz.) flour
0.14 litre ($\frac{1}{4}$ pt.) milk
Lemon rind, salt, pepper, parsley
28 g (1 oz.) breadcrumbs
2 eggs
1 tablespoon cream

METHOD

Pound the rabbit meat and pass through a sieve. Melt the butter in a saucepan, add the flour and cook together for a minute. Add the milk, stir and boil for a few minutes. Add the salt, pepper, parsley, meat, breadcrumbs and cream. Mix well and beat in the yolks of the eggs. Whip the whites until stiff and stir very lightly into the rest of the mixture. Pour into a greased soufflé dish, around which a greased paper has been tied to extend well above the sides of the dish. Bake 35 minutes in a moderate oven. Serve at once or it will drop.

Rabbit Pudding

Rabbit meat, boned and cut into small cubes
1 small onion
Salt, pepper
Suet crust made with 225 g (8 oz.) self-raising flour, 112 g (4 oz.) suet, pinch salt, water to mix

METHOD

Mix the flour, suet, salt into a stiff dough with water. Roll out and line a pudding basin, keeping enough for a lid. Roll the meat and chopped onion in seasoned flour and place in the basin. Half fill the basin with water and put on the lid. Cover with greaseproof paper and a scalded cloth and tie securely. Boil for 2 hours and serve with the basin wrapped in a napkin.

Jugged Rabbit

1 rabbit, jointed
1 tablespoon lemon juice
56 g (2 oz.) dripping
1 small onion stuck with cloves
Salt, pepper
$\frac{1}{2}$ teaspoon sugar
28 g (1 oz.) flour
1 wine glass port wine
Bouquet garni (spring parsley, 1 bay leaf, 1 blade mace, 2 cloves, 6 peppercorns, tied in muslin)
Forcemeat balls
Redcurrant jelly

METHOD

Sprinkle the rabbit with salt and pepper, saving the liver separately. Fry the joints in the dripping, place in a casserole with the onion, bouquet garni, lemon juice, sugar and wine. Cover with boiling stock, put on lid and cook in a slow oven for $3\frac{1}{4}$ hours. Make the forcemeat with the chopped liver, 112 g (4 oz.) breadcrumbs, 56 g (2 oz.) suet, 1 tablespoon parsley, pinch thyme, bound with beaten egg and seasoned well. Shape into small balls and fry in hot dripping. Fifteen minutes before serving, mix the flour to a paste with a little stock, add the liquor from the casserole. Boil and stir for a few minutes, pour back into the casserole and add the forcemeat balls. Place in the oven for a few minutes. Serve redcurrant jelly separately.

Rabbit in Tomato Sauce
(American Recipe)

1 large rabbit
2 tablespoons lard or butter
3 tablespoons flour
$1\frac{1}{2}$ cups tomato pulp and juice
1 large onion chopped finely
2 teaspoons salt
$\frac{1}{2}$ teaspoon pepper
3 cups boiling water

METHOD

Cut the rabbit into joints and dip in flour. Brown in a little fat. Put the lard or butter into a deep roasting pan, stir in the flour. Add the chopped onion and the tomato juice with the seasonings and boiling water. Cook for 5 minutes. When it boils, put in the browned rabbit, cover and simmer in the oven for an hour. The tomato cooks down and gives a good flavour to the rabbit.

Rabbit Livers with Bacon

Rabbit liver is very delicate and delicious with bacon and tomatoes. Fry the liver very lightly in the bacon fat and serve on small squares of fried bread also done in bacon fat.

Rabbit in Aspic

1 rabbit
0.8 litre ($1\frac{1}{2}$ pt.) stock
0.5 litre (1 pt.) aspic jelly
A 225 g (8 oz.) tin garden peas
2 hard boiled eggs
56 g (2 oz.) chopped ham
2-3 sliced tomatoes

METHOD
Cook the jointed rabbit in slightly salted stock or water for $1\frac{1}{2}$ hours, or until tender. Drain and remove the meat from the bones. Rinse a mould with cold water, line with a layer of nearly cold aspic jelly, allow to set. Decorate the jelly with slices of hard-boiled eggs and peas, cover gently with a layer of liquid jelly and allow to set. Arrange the rabbit meat, ham and rest of the eggs and peas in the mould, covering each layer with jelly. Allow to set before doing the next layer. When the mould is full, place in the refrigerator to set firmly. Serve on a dish decorated with slices of tomatoes.

Glossary

Antibiotics	Organic compounds used in fighting disease.
Balanced Ration	A ration that has the correct proportion of individual ingredients to provide for growth, production and reproduction.
Caecum	The blind gut at the head of the large intestine.
Cannibalism	Does eating their own young.
Cobby	Compact body shape, with a short neck and rather square appearance, as well as well-fleshed shoulders and meaty hindquarters.
Coprophagy	The rabbit consumes some of the droppings, the soft or night pellets, directly from its anus.
False or Pseudo-pregnancy	A period of 17 days during which the doe cannot conceive.
Grooming	Removing loose fur and dust from the rabbit's coat, by rubbing to and fro with the hands, using a neck-to-tail or reverse movement.
Heredity	The process by which characteristics are inherited from ancestors.
Hybrid	Rabbits bred from parents of different breeds, varieties or strains.
Kindling	Giving birth to young.
Lactation	The secretion and giving of milk.
Litter	A number of young being raised by one doe.
Malocclusion or Buck Teeth	A condition in which the teeth do not close properly.
Mature	Fully developed in all respects.
Prime Coat	Mature glossy coat free from moult, loose fur or partially grown fur.
Protein	Combination of amino acids essential to life.
Pure Bred	Recognised breed kept pure for generations.
Scours	The condition in which the rabbit passes its droppings or faecal pellets in a liquid or semi-liquid state, soiling the fur around the anus in doing so.
Sterile	Barren or infertile.
Tattoo	To mark permanently in the ear of rabbits, using a perforating instrument and Indian ink.
Vulva	External opening to the female organs.

Sources of Further Information

A Manual of Rabbit Farming, Marjorie E. P. Netherway.
Comprehensive text-book on rabbit production.

Green Foods for Rabbits and Cavies, F. R. Bell.
Detailed accounts of green foods suitable and unsuitable for rabbits.
Both books are obtainable from Fur and Feather Book Department, Idle, Bradford,
W. Yorks., BD10 8NL.

Fur and Feather.
A fortnightly periodical dealing extensively with rabbits for show, meat and pets.
Order from newsagent or by post from the above address.

Commercial Rabbit Association, Tyning House, Shurdington, Cheltenham,
Glos., GL51 5XF.
All matters relating to rabbit meat production.

British Rabbit Council, Purefoy House, 7 Kirkgate, Newark, Notts.
All matters relating to the Rabbit Fancy, and lists of local Rabbit Clubs.